JOURNEY TO FREEDOM

A CASEBOOK WITH MUSIC

EDITED BY

LANDON GERALD DOWDEY

THE SWALLOW PRESS INC.
1139 S. WABASH AVENUE, CHICAGO, ILLINOIS 60605

784.
4
Dowdey

Published by
The Swallow Press Incorporated
1139 South Wabash Avenue
Chicago, Illinois 60605

LIBRARY OF CONGRESS CATALOG CARD
NUMBER 70-84899

MYSTERY
The Call to Freedom   *1*

FEAR
The Urge to Run Away   *15*

COURAGE
Responding to the Risk   *21*

LOVE
The Reason for the Journey   *29*

SORROW
The Loneliness of Captivity   *35*

CHANGE
The Road of Promise   *41*

STRUGGLE
Participation in the Journey   *51*

HELP
The Weary Traveller   *60*

SUFFERING
The Cost of Travel   *64*

CREATION
Marriage to Life   *69*

THE KINGDOM
A Free Community   *75*

SING TO THE LORD A NEW SONG
Notes on the Art of Celebration   *82*
with a special musical supplement
SPIRITUALS FOR CITY PEOPLE   *94*

INDEX   *102*

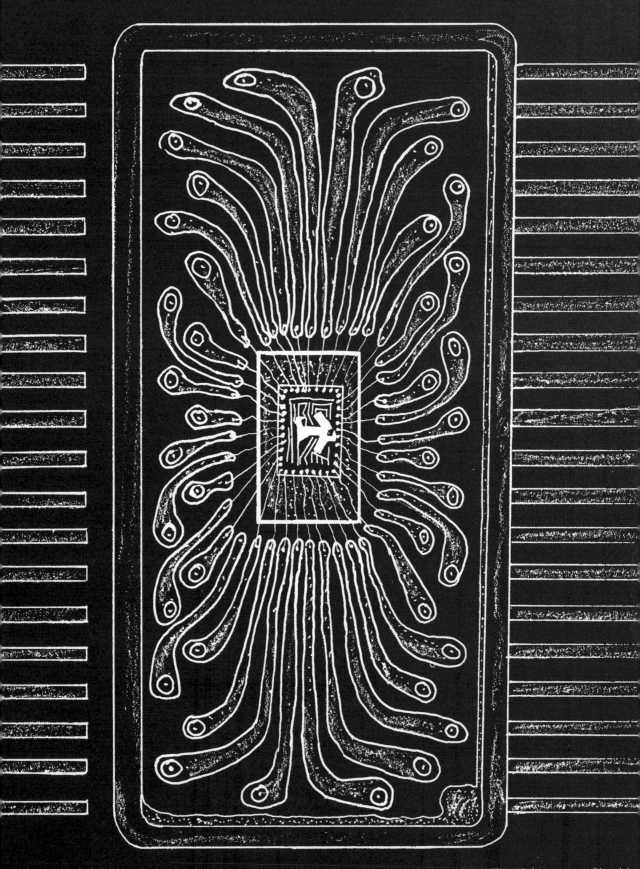

Not a scarab from Pharoah's tomb, but the latest revolutionary instrument of our society: The IC (Integrated Circuit), a tiny chip of synthetic crystal smaller than a postage stamp filled with scores of minute electronic devices; supplanter of the vaccum tube, the transistor, and a whole building full of wires and resistors; key to computerdom, space travel, and the limitless energy of the sun.

Mystery THE CALL TO FREEDOM

The Lord said to Móses: "I have witnessed

the affliction of my people in Egypt

"I have heard their cry of complaint against their slave drivers, so I know well what *they* are suffering

"Therefore I have come down to rescue them from the hands of the Egyptians and lead them out of that land into a good and spacious land flowing with *milk* and honey

"So you shall say to Pharaoh: Thus says the Lord: 'Israel is my son, my first born Hence I tell you: Let my son go, that *he* may serve me

"Let my people go that they may celebrate a feast to me *in* the desert "

Exodus 3,4,5 in Gregorian Chant [1]

WHAT'S THAT I HEAR

What's that I hear now	C/Em
ringin' in my ear?	A/D
I've heard that sound before	G/Em/D
What's that I hear now	C/Em
ringin' in my ear?	A/D
I hear it more and more	G/Em/D
It's the sound of freedom callin'	G/D
ringin' up to the sky!	C/F/D
It's the sound of	G
the old ways a-fallin'	D
You can hear it if you try!	C/D
You can hear it if you try!	C/D

What's that I see now
shinin' in my eyes?
I've seen that light before
What's that I see now
shinin' in my eyes?
I see it more and more
It's the light of freedom shinin'
shinin' up to the sky!
It's the light of the old ways a-fallin'
You can see it if you try!
You can see it if you try!

What's that I feel now
beatin' in my heart?
I've felt that beat before
What's that I feel now
beatin' in my heart?
I feel it more and more
It's the rumble of freedom callin'
climbin' up to the sky
It's the rumble of the old ways a-fallin'
You can feel it if you try!
You can feel it if you try!

Song by Phil Ochs [2]

UHURU

Uhu Uhuru Aiye Freedom!
Uhu Uhuru Aiye Freedom!

Uhu Uhuru Aiye Freedom!
Uhu Uhuru Aiye Freedom!

Uhu Uhuru Aiye Freedom!
Uhu Uhuru Aiye Freedom!

Uhuru!
Uhuru!

Uhuru O Sawaba!
Uhuru O Sawaba!
Uhuru O Sawaba!

Uhuru Aiye Aiye Aiye Freedom!

West African Chant as sung by Olatunji [3]

1,2,&3. An explanation of notes and symbols together with a general discussion of how to use this book will be found in the section titled SING TO THE LORD A NEW SONG beginning on page 82. An "s" after the note indicates that musical notation will also be found in the special supplement SPIRITUALS FOR CITY PEOPLE beginning on page 94 under the same numbering as the note.

WITHIN YOU AND WITHOUT YOU

We were talking
about the space between us all
and the people
who hide themselves behind a wall
of illusion—never glimpse the truth
then it's far too late
when they pass away

We were talking
about the love we all could share
when we find it
to try our best to hold it there
with our love.

With our love we could save the world
if they only knew.
Try to realize it's all within yourself
No one else can make you change
and to see
you're really only very small
and life flows on
within you and without you

We were talking
about the love that's gone so cold
and the people
who gain the world and lose their soul
They don't know—they can't see
are you one of them?

When you've seen beyond yourself
then you may find
peace of mind is waiting there
and the time will come
when you see we're all one
and life flows on
within you and without you

Chant by George Harrison[4]

BECAUSE ALL MEN
ARE BROTHERS

Because all men are brothers   *A/D/Bm/E/A*
wherever men may be   *C#/Gbm/C#/Gm*
one union shall unite them   *D/Bm/E/A*
forever proud and free   *C#/Gbm/C#/Gbm*

No tyrant shall defeat us   *D/E/Bm/A*
No nation strike us down   *D/Bm/F#*
All men who toil shall greet us   *E/D/E*
the whole wide world around   *A/D/Bm/E*

My brothers are all lovers
forever hand in hand
Where chimes the bell of freedom
there is my native land

My brother's cares are my cares
yellow, white or brown.
My brother's tears are my tears
the whole wide world around

Let every voice be thunder
Let every heart beat strong
Until all tyrants perish
our work shall not be done

Let not our memories fail us
the lost years shall be found
Let slavery's chains be broken
the whole wide world around

*Adaptation by Tom Glazer
of Passion Chorale of J.S. Bach[5]*

LISTEN!

Most people don't expect nothing important to come into them. They just expect to get up early—plow—rest—go turtle eggin' an' then back to bed. They never look up at the sky dark—or with stars—or blazing yellow with sunlight—and ask it, "Why? Why? Why?" . . .

That was the first word I learned to spell out at school. And I expected some answer. I felt there was something secret that I would find out and then it would all make sense . . . .

It would come into me. Through my eyes—see? Through my ears, through my skin. Like a net—see? If you don't spread it out, you won't catch nothing in it. But if you do, you might.

Tennessee Williams, Battle of the Angels

ENTER, REJOICE, AND COME IN

Enter, rejoice, and come in!   *C/C7*
Enter, rejoice, and come in!   *F/C*
Today will be a joyful day!   *F/C*
Enter, rejoice and come in!   *G7/C*

Open your ears to the song!
Open your ears to the song!
Today will be a joyful day!
Enter, rejoice, and come in!

Open your mind to what's real . . .

Open your heart to all men . . .

Make up your own verses

Song by Louise Ruspini[6S]

THE LORD'S SERVANT

I have endowed him with my spirit so that he may bring true justice to all nations; to open the eyes of the blind; to free captives from their prisons; and to deliver from their dungeons those who *live* in darkness.

I will say to the prisoners, "Come out," and to those who live in darkness, "Show yourselves." They will not hunger or thirst, nor shall the scorching sun and wind harm them, for he who pities *them* will lead them.

Isaiah 42, 49 in Gregorian Chant [1]

GO DOWN MOSES

When Israel was in Egypt land	Em/B7/Em
Let my people go!	B7/Em
Oppressed so hard	B7
They could not stand	Em
Let my people go!	B7/Em
Go down, Moses	Am
Way down in Egypt land	Em
Tell ol' Pharoah	C/Em
Let my people go!	B7/Em

Thus speaks the Lord, bold Moses said
Let my people go!
If not I'll strike your first born dead
Let my people go
Go down, Moses . . .

No more in bondage shall they toil
Let my people go!
Let them come out with Egypt's spoil
Let my people go!
Go down, Moses . . .

The foe shall not before them stand

Let my people go!
And they'll possess the promised land
Let my people go!
Go down, Moses . . .

O let us all from bondage flee
Let my people go!
And soon may all mankind be free
Let my people go!
Go down, Moses . . .

An Old Freedom Song [7S]

ABELACHAO

Una manana de sol radiante	Em

On one fine morning the sun was shining
Abelachao, abelachao
Abelachao, abelachao
Abelachao, chao, chao!
Abelachao, chao, chao!

Una manana de sol radiante	Am/Em

On one fine morning the sun was shining

Sali a buscar al opresor	B7/Em

I went out hunting the oppressor.

Es mi deseo seguir luchando
It's my desire to keep on fighting
Abelachao, abelachao
Abelachao, abelachao
Abelachao, chao, chao!
Abelachao, chao, chao!
Es mi deseo seguir luchando
It's my desire to keep on fighting
por la justicia y la verdad
for truth and justice in my land

Y si yo muero en el combate
And if I die in the battle
Abelachao, abelachao
Abelachao, abelachao
Abelachao, chao, chao!
Abelachao, chao, chao!
Y si yo muero en el combate
And if I die in the battle
toma en mis manos me fusil
There'll be a rifle in my hand

Soy cursillista toda la vida
I'm in the movement with all that's in me
Abelachao, abelachao
Abelachao, abelachao
Abelachao, chao, chao!
Abelachao, chao, chao!

Soy cursillista toda la vida
I'm in the movement with all that's in me
Y cursillista he de morir.
And I'll stay in it until I die.

Guatemalan Freedom Song[8S]

MORNING TRUMPET

How long, O Lord, how long	Dm
shall injustice mock the law	Gm
till we hear the trumpet sound	Dm/C
on that morning?	Dm/C/Dm
How long shall thieves and liars	Dm
be praised and held in awe	Gm
till we hear the trumpet sound	Dm/C
on that morning?	Dm/C/Dm
Shout O Glory O!	Am/F
A man stands up	Dm
against the crowd!	C/Dm
Can't you hear	Bb
that trumpet sound?	A

How long, O Lord, how long
will exploiters store up spoil
till we hear the trumpet sound
on that morning?
How long shall working people
get nothing for their toil
till we hear the trumpet sound
on that morning?
Shout O Glory O!...

How long, O Lord, how long
till the martyr's blood is paid
till we hear the trumpet sound
on that morning?
How long will evil prosper
and good men be dismayed
till we hear the trumpet sound
on that morning?
Shout O Glory O!...

O Rachel stop your weeping
the day is coming soon
when we'll hear the trumpet
sound on that morning.
The sorrow you have suffered
will then bring its reward

when we hear the trumpet sound
on that morning.
Adaptation of White Spiritual[9s]

> ### BREAD
> There are so many hungry people in the world that God cannot appear to them except in the form of bread.
> *M.K. Gandhi*

WHAT DOES YOUR GOD LOOK LIKE?

What does your God look like	Am/E/Am
my friend?	
What does your god look like?	C/D
What is his image in your eyes	Am/F/C
is he black or is he white?	D/E

Is he the face the glass gives back
when it's hangin' on the wall?
Is he the smile that masks the truth
of the mirror in the hall?

Is he your brother full of cheer
Is he your sister's smile?
But your brother and sister are angry now
Is your god still there the while?

Is he the altar trimmed in gold
Is he the music grand?
Or is he the old man by your side
with the dirt upon his hands?

Song by Patrick Mason[10S]

A WELL RESPECTED MAN

Cause he gets up in the morning	G/Bm/Em
and he goes to work at nine	G/Bm/Em
and he comes back home	G/Bm
at five-thirty	Em
gets the same train every time	G/Bm/Em
Cause his world is built on	C
punctuality, it never fails	Bm/C/D
And he's O so good!	G/Bm/Em
And he's O so fine!	G/Bm/Em
And he's O so healthy	G/Bm/Em
in his body and his mind!	G/Bm/Em
He's a well respected	C
man about town	D

Doing the best things   C
so conservatively.   D

And he likes his own back yard
and he likes his fags the best
cause he's better than the rest
and his armsweat smells the best
and he hopes to grab
his father's loot
and make the pad his own.

And he's O so good!...

Song by R. Davies[11]

THE SUFFERING SERVANT

He was spurned and avoided by men; a man of suffering, accustomed to infirmity; a man to make people hide their faces. He was despised, and we took no *account* of him.

Yet it was our infirmities he bore, our sufferings that he endured. We thought of him as one punished by God and brought low. But he was pierced for our offences, crushed *for* our sins.

Upon him was laid the punishment to make us whole, and through his wounds we were healed. We had all gone astray like sheep, each following his own way but the Lord laid upon him the *guilt* of us all.

Isaiah 53, in Gregorian Chant[1]

THERE BUT FOR FORTUNE

Show me a prison   G/Cm
show me a jail   G/Cm
show me a prison man   G/Em
whose face is growin' pale   A/D
and I'll show you a young man   G/Em
with many reasons why   C/Am
and there but for fortune   Bm/Em
may go you or I   A/D

Show me an alley, show me a train
show me a hobo
who sleeps out in the rain

and I'll show you a young man
with many reasons why
and there but for fortune
may go you or I

Show me the whisky
that stains on the floor
show me a drunken man
as he stumbles out the door
and I'll show you a young man
with many reasons why
and there but for fortune
may go you or I

Show me a country
where the bombs had to fall
show me the ruins
of the buildings once so tall
and I'll show you a young land
with so many reasons why
and there but for fortune
may go you or I

Song by Phil Ochs[12]

JONAH

We sail a ship   Dm
With a man named Jonah!
We sail a ship   C
With a man named Jonah!
We sail a ship   Dm
With a man named Jonah!
Earlye in the morning!   C/Dm

Lord, God, have mercy on us!   Dm
Lord, God, have mercy on us!   C
Lord, God, have mercy on us!   Dm
Earlye in the morning!   C/Dm

Who is the guilty one among us?...

Cast the lot and the number's Jonah's...

O Lord we've got to drown him...

Make up your own verses.

Adaptation of Sea Chanty by Ewald Bash [13s]

HOW IT FEELS

And I remember asking her one time
"Zia Teresa, how does it feel to die?"
—only a little girl would ask such a
question—and I remember her answer.
She said,"It's a lonely feeling."

Tennessee Williams, Orpheus Descending

MY COUNTRY TIS OF THY PEOPLE YOUR DYING

Now that your big eyes   D/B7
are finally open   A/D
Now that you're wondering   E/C
"How must they feel"   G/A
meaning them that you've chased   D/B7
across America's movie screens   A/D

Now that you're wondering   E/C
"How can it be real"   G/A
that the ones you've called   D
colorful, noble and proud   B7/A/D
in your school propaganda   E/C
they starve in their splendor   G/A
you must pardon my comment   D/B
I simply will render   A7/D

My country tis   D/G/A
of thy people   G/D
you're dying   G/A/D

Now that the long houses
breed superstition
you force us to send
our toddlers away
to your schools where they're taught
to despise their traditions
forbid them their languages
then further say

that American history
really began when Columbus
set sail out of Europe
and stress that the nation of legions
that conquered this land

are the biggest and bravest
and boldest and best and yet
where in your history books
is the tale of the genocide
basic to this country's birth?
of the preachers who lied
how the Bill of Rights failed
how a nation of patriots
returned to their earth?

and where will it tell
of the Liberty Bell
as it rang with a thud
o'er the hymns of a mud
and of brave Uncle Sam
in Alaska this year?

My country tis of thy people...

Hear how the bargain
was made for the West
with her shivering children
in zero degrees
blankets for your land
so the treaties attest
O well blankets for land
is a bargain indeed
and the blankets Uncle Sam
had collected from smallpox disease
dying soldiers that day
and the tribes were wiped out
and the history books censored
a hundred years of your statesmen
have felt it better this way

yet a few of the conquered
have somehow survived
their blood runs redder
though genes have been paled
from the Grand Canyon's Caverns
to craven sad hills
the wounded, the losers
the robbed sing their tale
from Los Angeles county
to upstate New York
the white nation fattens
while others grow lean
O the tricked and evicted
they know what I mean

My country tis of thy people...

The past it just crumbled
the future just threatens
our lifeblood shut up
in your chemical tanks
and out here you come bill of sale
in your hand and surprise in your
eyes that we're lacking in thanks

for the blessings of civilization
you've brought us
the lessons you've taught us
the ruin you've wrought us
see what our trust in America's
brought us.

My country tis of thy people...

Now that the pride
of the tribe receives charity
now that we're harmless and safe
behind laws
Now that my life's to be known
as your heritage now that even
the graves have been robbed

now that our own chosen way
is a novelty
hands on hearts we salute you
your victory, choke on your
blue white and scarlet hypocrisy
pitying the blindness
that you've never seen

the eagles of war whose wings
lent you glory they were never
no more than carrion crows
pushed the wrens from their nest
stole their eggs, changed their story
the mockingbird sings it
it's all that she knows

Ah, what can I do say a powerless few
with a lump in your throat
and a tear in your eye
can't you see that their poverty's
profiting you?

My country tis of thy people...

Chant by Buffy Sainte Marie[14]

NOVOCAIN

It's like when you go to the dentist, and the man is going to take your tooth...he squirts some stuff in your jaw called Novocain to make you think they're not doing anything to you. So you sit there, and because you got all that Novocain in your jaw, you suffer—"peacefully." Blood runnin' down your jaw, and you don't know what's happening 'cause someone has taught you to suffer—"peacefully."

The white man do the same thing to you in the street. When he wants to put some knots on your head, and take advantage of you, and don't have to be afraid of you fightin' back; to keep you from fightin' back, he get these ole religious Uncle Toms to teach you and me—they're just like Novocain —to suffer— "peacefully." Don't stop suffering. Just suffer "peacefully."

Malcolm X from one of his last speeches

THE PREACHER AND THE SLAVE

Long-haired preachers	E
come out every night	A/B7
try to tell you	
what's wrong and what's right	E
but when asked	
about something to eat	A/B7
they will answer	
with voices so sweet:	E
You will eat (You will eat)	
bye and bye (bye and bye)	B
in that glorious land	B7
in the sky (way up high)	E
Work and pray (Work and pray)	
live on hay (live on hay)	B7
you'll get pie in the sky	
when you die (that's a lie)	E
And the starvation army they play	
and they sing	
and they clap and they pray	
till they get	
all your coin on the drum	

then they tell you
when you're on the bum:
You will eat . . .

If you fight hard
for children and wife—
try to get
something good out of life—
you're a sinner
and bad man they tell.
When you die
you will sure go to hell.
You will eat . . .

Holy rollers and jumpers come out
and they jump
and they holler and shout
but when eating time comes around
they will say
you will eat on that glorious day.
You will eat . . .

Workingmen of all countries unite
Together we stand and we'll fight
when the world
and it's wealth we have gained
to the grafters
we'll sing this refrain:

You will eat (you will eat)
bye and bye (bye and bye)
when you've learned
how to cook and to fry (and to fry)
Chop some wood (chop some wood)
for your good (for your good)
and you'll eat
in the sweet bye and bye (that's no lie!)

*A Wobblie song by Joe Hill
to tune, "Sweet Bye and Bye" 16S*

THE HARDEST THING

Christ is merciless about the poor. He's
condemned them to live with us. The
poor have it hard, the saying goes. Well
we're the *hardest* thing they have.

Daniel Berrigan in Gregorian Chant[1]

WHEN I NEEDED A NEIGHBOR

When I needed a neighbor	Em
Were you there?	G
Were you there?	

When I needed a neighbor	Em/Bm
Were you there?	Em
And the creed and the color	G/Bm
And the name don't matter	Em/Bm
Were you there?	Em
Were you there?	Em/D/Em

I was cold, I was ragged. . .

When they put me in prison . . .

I was hungry, I was thirsty. . .

Wherever you travel, I'll be there. . .

Make up your own verses

Song by Sydney Carter 17S

THE INNOCENT SERVANT

Like a lamb led to slaughter, like a sheep
being sheared, he never spoke a word.
By force and by law he was taken with
none to plead his cause. He was snatch-
ed from the land of the living, and for
our sins he was *struck* down in death.

Isaiah 53 in Gregorian Chant[1]

BIRMINGHAM SUNDAY

Come round by my side	E
and I'll sing you a song	A
I'll sing it so softly	E
it'll do no one wrong	D/B
On Birmingham Sunday	E/B7
the blood ran like wine	E
and the choirs kept singing of	D/A
Freedom Freedom Freedom	E/D/G/A/E

That cold autumn morning
no eyes saw the sun
And Addie Mae Collins
her number was one
At an old Baptist church
there was no need to run
And the choirs kept singing of
Freedom Freedom Freedom

The clouds they were grey
and the autumn winds blew
And Denise McNair
brought the number to two

The Falcon of death
was a creature they knew
And the choirs kept singing of Freedom

The church it was crowded
but no one could see
That Cynthia Wesley's
dark number was three
Her prayers and her feelings
would shame you and me
And the choirs kept singing of Freedom

Young Carol Robertson
then entered the door
And the number her killers
had given was four
She asked for a blessing
but asked for no more
And the choirs kept singing of Freedom

On Birmingham Sunday
a noise shook the ground
And people all over
the earth turned around
For no one recalled
a more cowardly sound
And the choirs kept singing of Freedom

I mind my own buisness
I watch my T.V.
Complain about taxes
but pay anyway
in a civilized manner
my forefathers betray
who long ago struggled for Freedom.

*Words by Richard Farina to English folk song. Last
verse by Pete Seeger* [18s]

THE CITIES ARE BURNIN'

Lord, you know
these cities are burnin'
all over the U.S.A.
Oh, these cities are burnin' now
all over the U.S.A.
Yes, you know if these white folks
don't settle up soon
we all goin' to wake up
in Judgment Day!

You know the first was in Los Angeles
in a section they call Watts
then Newark, Detroit
and fifty more cities
all began to rock

I say these cities are burnin'
all over the U.S.A.
You know if these white folks
don't settle up soon
we all goin' to wake up
in Judgment Day.

You know God told Noah about it
the rainbow sign
there'll be no more water
but there'll be fire the next time
The Bible's fulfillin' now
all over the USA
And if these white folks
don't settle up soon
we all goin' to wake up
in Judgment day.

You know our Father
which art in heaven
Mr. Charlie owed me
a hundred dollars
and he don't give me but seven
Hallowed be thy name now
Kingdom come
hadn't taken that seven
you know I wouldn't have got none
That's why these cities are burnin' . .

Blues by Frederick Douglass Kirkpatrick [19]

A PIECE OF GROUND

When the white man	Am
first came here	G
from over the sea,	Am
he looked and he said	
"This is quite some country!"	C/E
He was mighty well pleased	Am
with this land that he found	C/F
And he said I will make it	Em
my own piece of ground.	Em7/Am

Now many's the battle
he still had to fight
and many's the family
who died in the night
cause many's the black man
who lived all around
all of them wanting
their own piece of land.

Then one fine day in 1883
gold was discovered in good quantity
Now the country was rich

and was richer than planned
and each people wanted
his own piece of land

Now this land is so rich
and it seems strange to me
that the black man whose labor
has helped it to be
cannot enjoy the fruits that abound
He's uprooted and kicked
from his own piece of land

Yet some people say
"Now don't you worry
You can always find jobs
in the white man's city "
But don't stay too long
and don't stay to eat
for you are bound to disturb
the white man in his sleep

White man don't sleep long
and don't sleep too deep
All your life and possessions
along with you keep
Cause I've heard a rumor
that's running around
of the Black man still wanting
his own piece of ground

Song by Jeremy Taylor as sung by Miriam Makeba [20]

THE REBEL

I am flesh of the flesh of these lowly, I am bone of their bone.

They have walked in fear of lawyers and of their jailers with their writs of summons and their handcuffs. I could have borne stripes on my body rather than the shame of my people.

I say to my people that they are holy, that they are august, despite their chains; that they are greater than those who hold them, and stronger and purer; that they have much need of courage, and to call on the name of their God. God the unforgetting, the dear God that loves the people for whom he died naked, suffering shame.

And I say to my people's masters: Beware! Beware of the thing that is coming. beware of the risen people. Did you think to conquer the people? Or that law is stronger than life and than men's desire to be free? We will try it out with

you, you that have harried and held, you that have bullied and bribed! Tyrants! Hypocrites! Liars!   *Padraic Pearce* [21]

WHO AM I

Who am I	C/G
to stand and wonder	C/G
to wait	D
while the wheels of fate	C/G
slowly grind my life away?	C/G
Who am I?	C/G
There were some things	G
that I liked one time	C
but the dreams are gone	G
that I thought were mine	C
and the hidden tears	G
that once could fall	C
now burn inside	G
at the thought of all	C
the years of waste	G
the years of crime	C
the passions of a heart so blind	G/C
Think back — but even still	G/C
as I stand exposed	G
the feelings are felt	C
and I cry	G
into the echo of my loneliness	C/D/G
Who am I . . .	C/G

What a nothing I've made of life
The empty words, the cowards flight
to be pushed and passed
from hand to hand
never daring to speak
never daring to stand
and the emptiness of my family's eyes
remind me over and over of lies
and promises and deeds undone
and now again I want to run
but now
there is nowhere to run to
Who am I . . .

*Song by Joe McDonald
as sung by Country Joe and the Fish* [22]

LA PEREGRINACION

Y que yo he de decir	Dm/A7
And what I wanted to say	
Que yo estoy cansado	
is I'm pretty darn tired	
Que el camino es largo	
It's a long weary road	
Y no se ve el fin	Dm
and you can't see the end.	

Desde Delano voy
I go from Delano
Hasta Sacramento
towards Sacramento
Hasta Sacramento
Towards Sacramento
Mis derechos a pelear.
to fight for what's mine.

Yo no vengo a cantar
I do not come for singing
Porque mi voz sea buena
even though my voice is good
Ni tampoco a llorar
Nor do I come for crying
Mi mal estar
of the troubles I have.

Mi Virgencita
My dear Virgin Mary
Guadelupana
of Guadelupe
Oye estos pasos
Listen to these footsteps
Que todo el mundo los sabrá.
all the world is going to know them.

Desde Delano...
I go from Delano. . .

A song of the Delano Grape Strike by Augustín Lira.
Translated by Richard J. Carr. [23]

EVERYBODY'S GOT A RIGHT TO LIVE

Everybody's got a right to live	C/F/C
Everybody's got a right to live	G
And before this campaign fails	C
We'll all go down in jail	F
Everybody's got a right to live.	C/F/C

On my way to Washington	C
feelin' awful sad	
thinkin' about an income	
that I never had	F/C
Everybody's got a right to live. . .	F/C

Black man picked the cotton
a long time ago
he has been the victim
since they brought him to this shore
Everybody's got a right to live. . .

Black man dug the pipeline
hewed down the pines
gave his troubles to Jesus
kept on toeing the line
Everybody's got a right to live. . .

Black man dug the ditches
both night and day
Black man did the work
white man got the pay
Everybody's got a right to live. . .

Now look a-here Congress
this is a brand new day
No more full time work
and part time pay
Everybody's got a right to live. . .

I want my share of silver
I want my share of gold
I want my share of Justice
to save my dyin' soul!
Everybody's got a right to live. . .

Song by Frederick Douglass Kirkpatrick [19]

DREAMERS

You remember those two! I once mentioned them to you. You said, "They're harmless dreamers and they're loved by the people." — "What," I asked . . . "is harmless about the love of the people? Revolution only needs good dreamers who remember their dreams, and love of the people belongs safely only to you, their Generalissimo."

Tennessee Williams, Camino Real

THROUGH THE BITTER LAND

As they walk through the bitter land they make it a place of springs. The rains add their blessing and it brings forth new life, and growing in strength, they move on.

Handful of strangers in a foreign land
protected by God alone
Rebuild ruined cities
and bind up broken hearts
Bring garlands of joy to the poor.

Truth and kindness shall meet at last
while justice and peace embrace
as truth reaches up
from the bowels of the earth
and justice leans down from above.

Adaptation of a White Spiritual [24]

LORD OF THE DANCE

I danced in the morning	G/Em
when the world was begun	Bm/Em
and I danced in the moon	Am
and the stars and the sun	Bm
I came down from heaven	G/Em
and I danced on the earth	Bm/Em
in Bethlehem	Am/Bm
I had my birth	Am/G

Dance then wherever you may be	Bm/Em
I am the Lord	G/Bm
of the dance said he	Am/D
And I'll lead you all	G/Em
wherever you may be	G/Bm
I'll lead you all	Am/Bm
in the dance said he	G

I danced for the scribe
and the Pharisee
but they would not dance
and they would not follow me
I danced for the fishermen
for James and John
They came with me
and the dance went on
Dance then. . .

I danced on the sabbath
and I cured the lame
the holy people said
it was a shame
They whipped and they stripped
and they hung me high
and they left me there
on a cross to die
Dance then. . .

I danced on a Friday
when the sky turned black

it's hard to dance
with the devil on your back
They buried my body
and they thought I'd gone
but I am the dance
and I still go on
Dance then. . .

They cut me down
and I leaped up high
I am the life
that'll never, never die
I'll live in you if you'll live in me
I am the Lord of the dance said he
Dance then. . .

Song by Sydney Carter [25]

COME AND GO WITH ME

Come and go with me to that land	E/E7
Come and go with me to that land	A/E
Come and go with me to that land	C#m
Where I'm bound.	F#m/B
Come and go with me to that land	E/E7
Come and go with me to that land	A/F#
Come and go with me to that land	E/B7
Where I'm bound	E/A/E

There'll be Freedom in that land
Lots of freedom in that land
Freedom in that land where I'm bound
Come and go with me to that land . . .

There'll be justice in that land. . .

There'll be singin' in that land. . .

There'll be lovin' in that land. . .

Adaptation of a Negro Spiritual [26S]

I CANNOT COME

A certain man held a feast	D/G
on his fine estate in town	D
He laid a festive table	A7/Em7/A7
and wore a wedding gown	D/A7/D
He sent invitations	D7/G
to his neighbors far and wide	D/A7/D
but when the meal was ready	A7/Em7/A7
each of them replied:	D

I cannot come	D
I cannot come to the banquet.	D7/G
Don't trouble me now	D/A7/D
I have married a wife	A7/Em7/A7

I have bought me a cow   *D/Em/D7*
I have fields and commitments   *G*
that cost a pretty sum   *D/Em/D*
Pray hold me excused   *A7*
I cannot come   *D*

The master rose up in anger
called his servants by name
said "Go into the town
fetch the blind and the lame
fetch the peasant and the pauper
for this I have willed
my banquet must be crowded
and my table must be filled"
I cannot come. . .

When all the poor had assembled
there was still room to spare
so the master demanded
"Go search everywhere
to the highways and the byways
and force them to come in
My table must be filled
before the banquet can begin"
I cannot come. . .

Now God has written a lesson
for the rest of mankind
if we're slow in responding
He may leave us behind
He's preparing a banquet
for that great and glorious day
when the Lord and master calls us
be certain not to say
I cannot come. . .

Song by Miriam Therese Winter 27

WE'RE GONNA ROLL

We're gonna roll, we're gonna roll   *G*
we're gonna roll the movement on   *D7*
we're gonna roll, we're gonna roll
we're gonna roll the movement on   *G*
If the boss is in the way
we're gonna roll it over him
we're gonna roll it over him   *D7*
we're gonna roll it over him   *G*
If the boss is in the way
we're gonna roll it over him
we're gonna roll the movement on   *D7/G*

If the sheriff's in the way. . .

If its Congress in the way. . .

Make up your own verses. . .

Adaptation of "Roll the Union On," which was adaptation of Negro Spiritual, "Roll the Chariot On" 28S

THE SPIRIT IS MOVIN'

Well, well, well   *Am*
who's that a callin'?   *E/Am*
well, well, well   *Dm*
take your neighbor's hand   *E7*
well, well, well   *Am*
daylight's a dawnin'   *E/Am*
cause the spirit is a movin'   *C*
all over the land   *E7*

The spirit is a movin'   *C*
to set men free
the spirit is a callin'   *Em*
us all to liberty
Brothers and sisters side by side   *A7/Dm*
all standin' up and they won't hide   *E7*
Well, well, well. . .

A new world's comin'
and it won't be long
in this new world
everybody belongs
so let's all help the spirit to move
shake off the dust
and let this new world groove
Well, well, well. . .

The people are a movin'
all over the land
and they're all travelin'
by the spirit's command   .
they can't sit still; they just won't wait
they're workin' with their neighbors
to rid this old world of hate
Well, well, well. . .

Let's all stick together
and work for that day
cryin' prayin' laughin' hopin'
all of the way
when it comes, we'll all be there
to join in the good times
everybody will share
Well, well, well. . .

Adaptation of Negro Spiritual by John Snyder 29S

Fear

TO TREMBLE

I tremble at the shouts of the foe
My heart is quaking within me
The terror of death is upon me
The horror is overwhelming

If I had wings like a dove
I'd fly away to where it's restful
I'd escape from all this conflict
taking refuge safe in the desert

There I would soon find a shelter
from the winds that rage about me
safe from the violent storm
and from evil plotting tongues

For I can see nothing but violence
and strife within the city
Its streets are never free
from tyranny and deceit

Psalm 55 in metrical chant [31]

YESTERDAY

Yesterday, all my troubles	C/E
seemed so far away	Am
Now it seems	F/G
they're here to stay	F/C
Oh, I believe in yesterday	Am/D/F/C

Suddenly, I'm not half the man
I used to be
There's a shadow hanging over me
Oh yesterday came suddenly

Why she had to go	E/Am
I don't know	Dm
She wouldn't say	G/C
I said something wrong	E/Am
now I long for yesterday	Dm/G/C

Yesterday, love was such
an easy game to play
Now I need a place to hide away
Oh, I believe in yesterday

Song by John Lennon and Paul McCartney [4]

THE URGE TO RUN AWAY

TO RUN

The picture of the commuter fleeing from the fierce activity and excitement of the city to the bucolic banalities of the suburbs. . . a mass escape from responsibility into little isolated worlds of conformity. . . . What is most sought after is amnesia—forgetfulness—forgetfulness of cannibalistic competition, political corruption, and, most of all, suffering humanity.

To avoid seeing Lazarus at the city gate, these people avoid the city. . . .

If you think this is a harsh judgment, I ask you to consider the pathological reaction produced in these enclaves of residential and religious respectability when they are threatened with a reminder of their common humanity, like integrated housing.

Landon Gerald Dowdey, Communities of Interest in the Modern City [32]

LITTLE BOXES

Little boxes on the hillside	C
little boxes made of ticky tacky	F/C
little boxes on the hillside	G7
little boxes all the same	C/G7
There's a green one	C
and a pink one	
and a blue one, and a yellow one	F/C
and they're all made	
out of ticky tacky	G7
and they all look just the same	C/G7/C

And the people in the houses
all go to the university
and they all get put in boxes
little boxes all the same.
And there's doctors, and there's lawyers
and bus'ness executives
and they're all made out of ticky tacky
and they all look just the same

And they all play on the golf course
and drink their martinis dry
and they all have pretty children

and the children go to school.
And the children go to summer camp
and then to the university
and they all get put in boxes
and they all come out the same.

And the boys go into bus'ness
and marry and raise a family
and they all get put in boxes
little boxes all the same.
There's a green one, and a pink one
and a blue one, and a yellow one
And they're all made out of ticky tacky
and they all look just the same.

Song by Malvina Reynolds [33]

THE SAFETY OF SLAVERY

Pharaoh was already near when the Israelites looked up and saw that the Egyptians were on the march in pursuit of
them. In great fright they cried out to
the Lord, and com*plained* to Moses:

"Were there no burial places in Egypt
that you had to bring us out here to die
in the desert? Why did you do this to us?
Why did you bring us *out* of Egypt?

"Did we not tell you this in Egypt, when
we said, 'Leave us alone. Let us serve *the*
Egyptians'?

"Far better for us to be slaves of the
Egyptians than to die *in* the desert."

Exodus 14 in Gregorian Chant [1]

MR. BLUE

Good morning, Mr. Blue	C
We've got our eyes on you	
The evidence is clear	Bb
that you've been cheating	C
You like to steal away	
and wile away the day	
You like to spend	Bb
an hour dreaming	C
What will it take	A
to whip you into line?	C/A
A broken heart?	C/A
A broken mind?	C/A
It can be arranged	Em/A

Step softly, Mr. Blue
We know what's best for you
We know where your precious dreams

will take you
You've got a slot to fill
and fill that slot you will
You'll learn to love it
or we'll break you
What will it take . . .

Be careful, Mr. Blue
This phase you're going through
It'll lead you nowhere else
but to disaster
Excuse us while we grin
You've worn our patience thin
It's time to show you who is master
What will it take . . .

Don't worry, Mr. Blue
We'll take good care of you
Just think of it as sense
and not surrender
But never think again
that you can think again
For you will get something
you'll remember
What will it take . . .

Song by Tom Paxton [34]

NOT TO FEEL

Men pity and love each other more
deeply than they permit themselves to
know . . . Fear and evasion are the two
little beasts that chase each other's tails
in the revolving wire cage of our nervous
world. They distract us from feeling too
much about things.

Tennessee Williams, The Timeless World of a Play

YOU'VE GOT TO HIDE YOUR LOVE AWAY

Everywhere people stare	D/A/G/D
each and every day	G/C/G
I can hear them laugh at me	D/A/G/D
and I hear them say—	G/C/G/A
Hey, you've got to hide	D/G
your love away!	A
Hey, you've got to hide	D/G
your love away!	A

How can I even try
I can never win?

Hearing them
seeing them
in the state I'm in!

Hey, you've got to hide
your love away . . .

How can you say to me
love will find a way?
Gather round all you clowns
let me hear you say—

Hey, you've got to hide
your love away . . .

Song by John Lennon and Paul McCartney [4]

HIDE YOUR HEART, LITTLE HIPPIE

Hide your heart, little hippie	Gmaj7/C
hide your heart	G/C/G
Hide your heart, little hippie	Gmaj7/C
hide your heart.	D7
Stay remote and uninvolved	Gmaj7/C
keep your problems all unsolved	Gmaj7/C
Hide your heart, little hippie	G/D7
hide your heart.	G/C/G

Talk the talk, little hippie
talk the talk
Talk the talk, little hippie
talk the talk.
Water down what you would say
wrap it in some tired cliche.
Talk the talk, little hippie
talk the talk.

Walk on by, little hippie
walk on by
Walk on by, little hippie
walk on by.
With your head up in the sky
are you happy or just high?
Walk on by, little hippie
walk on by.

Do you see, little hippie
do you see
Do you see, little hippie
do you see?
Are the shades you hide behind
like some curtain for your mind?
Do you see, little hippie
do you see?

Watch the styles, little hippie
watch the styles
Watch the styles, little hippie
watch the styles.
Sandals used to cut your skin.
Aren't you glad now boots are in?
Watch the styles, little hippie
watch the styles.

Song by Len Chandler [35]

NOT TO CRY

ALVARO: I am ashame of what happen. Crying is not like a man. Did anyone see me?
SERAFINA: Nobody saw you but me. To me it don't matter.
ALVARO: You are simpatica, molto! It was not just the fight that makes me break down. It was like this all today! . . . The wages have been garnishee!— All in one day is too much! I boil, I cry, and I am ashame but I am not able to help it!—Even a Wop truckdriver's a human being! And human beings must cry . . .
SERAFINA: Yes, they must cry. I couldn't cry all day but now I have cried and I am feeling much better.

Tennessee Williams, The Rose Tattoo

PACK UP YOUR SORROWS

No use cryin', talkin' to a stranger	C/F
namin' the sorrow you've seen	C/G
too many sad times	C
too many bad times	F
nobody knows what you mean.	C/G/C

But if somehow you could	C
pack up your sorrows	F
and give them all to me	C/G
you would lose them	C
I know how to use them	F
give them all to me.	C/G/C

No use ramblin', walkin' in the shadow
trailin' a wanderin' star
no one beside you
no one to hide you
nobody knows where you are
But if somehow . . .

No use gamblin', runnin' in the darkness
lookin' for a spirit that's free
too many wrong times
too many long times
nobody knows what you see
But if somehow . . .

No use roamin', lyin' by the roadside
seeking a satisfied mind
too many highways
too many byways
and nobody walkin' behind
But if somehow . . .

Song by Richard Farina and Pauline Marden 36

RELEASE

While I kept it secret
I groaned all the day
My bones were wasting away
and my heart grew parched as stubble

But now I have faced the truth
and you have relieved my guilt
You have raised me from the dead
restored me to life from the grave

Psalms 32 and 139 in metrical chant 31

WOMAN AT THE WELL

Jesus met the woman at the well   D
Jesus met the woman at the well   G/D
Jesus met the woman at the well G/F#/Bm
and he told her ev'rything   E/E7
she'd ever done.   A

He said: "Woman, woman
where is your husband? . . .
I know ev'rything you've ever done."

She said: "Jesus, Jesus
I ain't got no husband. . . .
And you don't know everything
I've ever done. . . ."

He said: "Woman, woman
you've got five husbands. . . .
And the one you have now
he's not your own. . . ."

She said: "This man, this man
he must be a prophet . . . .
He done told me ev'rything
I've ever done. . . ."

Gospel Song as sung by Mahalia Jackson 37

TO LIE

He must flatter and be pleasant, endure
petty insults with a smile, shut his eyes
to wrong . . . . He must not criticize, he
must not complain. Patience, humility,
and adroitness . . . replace impulse,
manliness, and courage. With this sacrifice there is an economic opening . . .
the right to share in modern culture. The
price of culture is a lie.

W.E.B. Du Bois, The Souls of Black Folk

DYING

Polite smiles	Em
good manners	A
pleasant talk	Em/A
Belonging	Em
to all the in groups	A
doing	Em
all the right things	A
Dying	Em
Dying	B
Dying	Am7
Afraid to live	Em/A/Em

Sensible
reasonable
self-controlled
Above the crowd
who curse and shout
and lose control
Dying . . .

Safe from fools
Safe from chance
Safe from blame
Secure
on an island
where nobody
cries
Dying . . .

Insulated
elevated
isolated
Comforted
by the comfortable
bromides
of conformity
Dying . . .

So sure
so cool
so admired
Ending
the job
of avoiding life
with a bullet
Dying . . .

Contemporary chant
by Landon Dowdey
and Ozzie Gontang [38]

WE DIDN'T KNOW

"We didn't know"	E
said the Burgomeister	A
"about the camps	E
on the edge of town	B7/E
It was Hitler and his crew	A
that tore the German nation down	E/B7/E
We saw the cattle cars it's true	C#m
and maybe they carried	E
a Jew or two	B7/E
they woke us up	C#m
as they rattled through	
but what did you	E
expect me to do?"	B7/E

We didn't know at all	E
We didn't see a thing	A/E
You can't hold us to blame	
What could we do?	F#/B7
It was a terrible shame	E
But we can't bear the blame	A
Oh, no, not us, we didn't know	E/A/B7/E

"We didn't know"
said the congregation
singing a hymn
in their church of white
"The Press was full of lies about us
Preacher told us we were right
The outside agitators came
They burned some churches
and put the blame
on decent southern people's names
to set our colored people aflame
and maybe some of our boys got hot
and a couple of niggers
and reds got shot
They should have stayed

where they belong
and preacher would've told us
if we'd done wrong
We didn't know at all . . . "

"We didn't know"
said the puzzled voter
watching the President on T V
"I guess we've got to
drop those bombs
if we're gonna keep South Asia free
The President's such a peaceful man
I guess he's got some kind of plan
They say we're torturing
prisoners of war
but I don't believe that stuff no more
Torturing prisoners is a communist game
and you can bet they're doing the same
I wish this war was over and thru
but what do you expect me to do?
We didn't know at all . . . "

Song by Tom Paxton [39]

TO HIDE

It is dangerous to go out
into this hellish world
but it is still more dangerous
to hide in the bushes

There is a smell on earth
of a universal Dallas . . .

You are shooting not at King
but at your conscience . . .

And a second of the Kennedys falls . . .

When a nation
is going dangerously insane
it cannot be cured of its troubles
by hastily prescribed calm

Yevgeny Yevtushenko

NOWHERE MAN

He's a real nowhere man	C/G
sitting in his nowhere land	F/C
making all his nowhere plans	Dm/Fm6
for nobody	C
Doesn't have a point of view	C/G
knows not where he's going to	F/C

Isn't he a bit like you and me?   *Dm/Fm6/C*
Nowhere man, please listen   *Em/F*
You don't know   *Em*
what you're missing   *F*
Nowhere man   *Em*
the world is at your   *Dm*
command!   *G*

He's as blind as he can be
Just sees what he wants to see
Nowhere man, can you see me at all?

Nowhere man, don't worry
Take your time, don't hurry
Leave it all til somebody else
lends you a hand

Doesn't have a point of view
Knows not where he's going to
Isn't he a bit like you me?

Nowhere man, please listen
You don't know what you're missing.
Nowhere man
the world is at your command!

He's a real nowhere man
sitting in his nowhere land
·making all his nowhere plans
for nobody
making all his nowhere plans for nobody
making all his nowhere plans
for nobody

Song by John Lennon and Paul McCartney 4

You can imagine what a howling, shocking nuisance this man was to both Neroes and whites. Once Malcolm fastened on you, you could not escape.

Ossie Davis

WHERE YOU GONNA RUN TO?

O sinner man   *Dm*
where you gonna run to?
O sinner man   *C*
where you gonna run to?
O sinner man   *Dm*
where you gonna run to?
On that day of truth!   *A7/Dm*

You run to your rock
Your rock, it is a meltin'. . .

You run to your games
Your games they are all pointless. . .

You run to a party
at the party no one's listening. . .

You run to your money
Your money is a burnin'. . .

Make up your own verses.

Adaptation of a White Spiritual 40S

TO TELL THE TRUTH

Now, we all knew these things as well as Malcolm did, but we also knew what happened to people who stick their necks out and say them. And if all the lies we tell ourselves by way of extenuation were put into print, it would constitute one of the great chapters in the history of man's justifiable cowardice in the face of other men.

But Malcolm kept snatching our lies away. He kept shouting the painful truth we whites and blacks did not want to hear from all the housetops. And he wouldn't stop for love nor money.

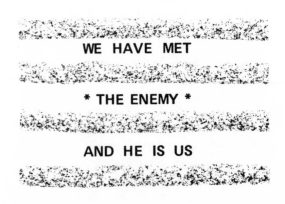

WE HAVE MET

* THE ENEMY *

AND HE IS US

Courage

Wade in the water! Wade in the water, children! Wade in the water! Trust in the Lord

and wade in!   *He spoke and divided the sea in two!* Wade in the water!

Allowing all his people · to pass on through! Wade in the water!

He spoke and the water
flowed back again.Wade in the water!
And drowned the oppressors
pursuing them.Wade in the water!
Wade in the water . . .

The enemy's great
but my captain's strong.
Wade in the water!
I'm marchin' to the city
and the road ain't long.
Wade in the water!
Wade in the water . . .

Adaptation of Negro Spiritual [41]

BE YOURSELF

In those sombre forests of his striving
his own soul rose before him, and he
saw himself, darkly as through a veil;
and yet he saw in himself some faint
revelation of his power, of his mission.
He began to have a dim feeling that,
to attain his place in the world, he must
be himself, and not another.

W.E.B. DuBois, The Souls of Black Folk

GEORGE FOX

There's a light that is shining	*Em/C*
in the heart of a man	*A/C*
It's the light that was shining	*Em/C*
when the world began	*A/B11*
There's a light that is shining	*Em/C*
in the Turk and the Jew	*A/C*
and a light that is shining	*Em/C*
friend, in me and in you	*B11/E*
Old leather breeches	*G#m*
shaggy, shaggy locks!	*F#m/B7*
Old leather breeches	
shaggy, shaggy locks!	*E*
With your old leather breeches	*G#*
and your shaggy,shaggy locks	*A/F#m*
you are pulling down the pillars	*E/B7*
of the world, George Fox!	*A/E*

"If we give you a pistol
will you fight for the Lord?"
"You can't kill the devil
with a gun or a sword."
"Will you swear on the Bible?"
"I will not," said he
"For the truth is as holy
as the Book to me."

Old leather breeches . . .

There's an ocean of darkness
and I drowned in the night
till I came through the darkness
to the ocean of light
And the light is forever
and the light will be free
and I'll walk in the glory
of the light said he
Old leather breeches . . .

Song by Sydney Carter [42]

WHEN MAMA PARKS SAT DOWN THE WHOLE WORLD STOOD UP.

Between wars—civil wars that is—every-body just kind of sat around and talked about the way they were treatin' each other, nobody really doing nothin' about it. Till one day a little old lady took a seat in the front of the bus. The bus driv-er told her to move to the back, the reason being the color of her skin or somethin' like that.

Well, Ol' Mama Parks didn't move, but the whole world did.

Song introduction by the Bay Singers

UNION MAID

There once was a union maid	A7/D
she never was afraid of goons	G/D/Em
and ginks and company finks	A7/D/Bm
and the deputy sheriffs	E7
that made the raid	A7
She went to the union hall	D
when a meeting it was called	G/D
and when the company boys	Em/A7/D
came round	Bm
she always stood her ground	Em/A7/D

Oh, you can't scare me	G
I'm sticking to the union	D
I'm sticking to the union	A7
I'm sticking to the union	D
Oh, you can't scare me	G
I'm sticking to the union	D
I'm sticking to the union	A7
till the day I die	D

This union maid was wise
to the tricks of the company spies

She couldn't be fooled
by the company stools
she'd always organize the guys
she'd always get her way
when she struck for higher pay
she'd show her card
to the National Guard
and this is what she'd say

Oh, you can't scare me. . .

Words by Woodie Guthrie to tune of "Red Wing" [43]

LAUGHIN' FOOL

Why should we be discouraged because somebody laughs at us today? Who can tell what tomorrow will bring forth? Did they not laugh at Moses, Christ, and Mo-hammed?

Marcus Garvey

We don't mind people laughin'	C/Am
at the worn out clothes we wear	C
we got everything	
when we got freedom	Am
and you're just a laughin' fool!	F/C/G7

You may laugh at our bushy hair
and the worn out clothes we wear
we got everything
when we got freedom
and you're just a laughin' fool!

You may laugh at the holes in our shoes
you may buy clothes
and shoes brand new
we got everything. . .

You may laugh at us inside
when you see us goin' by
but you're enjoyin'
some of the benefits
that we have died for— oh yes.

Medgar Evers and Emmett Till
were true examples of courage and will
they had everything when they . . .

You know they stabbed Dr. King
burned up his house and everything
I heard him say you know it's true
forgive them Jesus
for they know not what they do—
he had everything when he. . .

When the segregation is broken down
you will see every Tom in town
sittin' at lunch counters
smokin' big cigars
and sayin' "look what we have done."
Try to take the credit from dead heroes
moldin' in the ground.

Song by Frederick Douglass Kirkpatrick [44s]

THE ONE ESSENTIAL

// Few are willing to brave the disapproval
of their fellows, the censure of their col-
leagues, the wrath of their society. Moral
courage is a rarer commodity than
bravery in battle or great intelligence.
Yet it is the one essential, vital quality
for those who seek to change a world
that yields painfully to change.

Robert F. Kennedy

AIN'T GONNA LET NOBODY TURN ME ROUND

Ain't gonna let nobody   *D*
turn me round
turn me round, turn me round   *A7/D*
Ain't gonna let nobody
turn me round
Gonna keep on a walkin'   *A7*
Keep on a talkin'
Marchin' on to Freedom Land   *D*

Ain't gonna let Nervous Nelly
turn me round . . .

Ain't gonna let Mr. Charlie
turn me round . . .

Freedom Song [45]

KEEP YOUR EYE ON THE PRIZE

Everything that was written long ago in
the scriptures was meant to teach us
something about hope from the examples scripture gives of how people
who did not give up were helped by God.

St. Paul in letter to Romans, Chap. 15

Paul and Silas bound in jail   *Am*
had no money for to go their bail   *E7/Am*
keep your eye on the prize
Hold on! Hold on!   *E7/Am/G/Am*
Hold on! Hold on!   *E/Am*
Keep your eye on the prize   *G/Am*
Hold on! Hold on!   *E7/Am/G/Am*

Paul and Silas began to shout
the jail door opened
and they walked right out.
Keep your eye on the prize. . .

The only chain a man can stand
is that chain of hand in hand
Keep your eye on the prize. . .

The only thing that we did was wrong
was stayin' in the wilderness too long
Keep your eye on the prize. . .

Freedom Song. [46S]

KEEP GOIN' ON

My father got lynched. My father got
lynched. My father got shot twelve times.
That was thirty-five years ago. My mother died because she couldn't take care
of us. We had six children in the family.
So they put all of us in an orphan home.
I never seen my mother again. . . .O.K.
But one thing I had to do. I had to keep
goin' on. I can't stop. Look-a-here: When
Jesus was on the cross and they were
hittin' him and kept hittin' him he still
kept goin' on! and that's what we got
to do.

*Transcript of a Rap & Suds Session at Build Black,
Inc. April, 1968.* [47]

MARY DON'T YOU WEEP

So Moses stretched out his hand over
the sea, and at dawn the sea flowed back
to its normal depth. As the water flowed
back, it covered the chariots and chario-
teers of Pharaoh's whole army which had
followed the Israelites into the sea. Thus
the Lord saved Israel on that day from
the power of the Egyptians.

Exodus 14

O Mary don't you weep   *E/B7*
don't you mourn   *E*
O Mary don't you weep   *E*
don't you mourn
Pharaoh's army got drownded   *A/E*
O Mary don't you weep   *B7/E*

When death seemed sure
and all seemed lost
the tomb opened wide
and life burst forth
Pharaoh's army got drownded
O Mary don't you weep!
O Mary don't you weep . . .

Jesus crossed over
from death to life
to show we can make it
through storm and strife
Pharaoh's army got drownded . . .

Flowers are blooming
sing hallelu!
The sun is up
and the world is new
Pharaoh's army got drownded . . .

The word is true
it will not fade
Don't be afraid
we've got it made
Pharaoh's army got drownded . . .

Adaptation of Negro Spiritual [47S]

How many times
must the sick look up
and find that there's no one to care?
How many times
must I stumble and fall
before you offer your hand?
How many times
must I reach through these bars
before you hand me the keys?
The answer my friend . . .

How many branches
still cling to the vine
without their share of its life?
How many men
still pray to their god
with hate in their hearts like a knife?
How many years
will it take till we know
the hurt we cause by our pride?
The answer my friend . . .

Why can't we sing
a song full of love
in a spirit open to all?
Why can't we have
a world without hate
so no one else has to die?
Why can't we find
somewhere in our lives
the courage we need just to try?
The answer my friend . . .

New words to "Blowing in the Wind" [48]

LIVING IN ALL MEN

How many years   *D/G*
must my people exist   *D*
before they know   *G*
they are one?   *A*
How many times   *D/G*
must their blood be shed   *D/Bm*
before they know   *D/Em*
that it's mine?   *A*
How many times   *D/G*
will you break my bread   *D*
before you give me to eat?   *G/A*
The answer my friend   *G/A*
is living in all men   *D/Bm*
The answer is living in all men   *G/A/D*

MOVING ON

KILROY: The deal is rugged. D' you know what I mean?

QUIXOTE: Who knows better than I what a rugged deal it is! Will you take some advice?

KILROY: Brother, at this point on the Camino I will take anything which is offered!

QUIXOTE: Don't! Pity! Your! Self! The wounds . . . the many offences our egos have to endure, being housed in bodies that age and hearts that grow tired, are better accepted with a tolerant smile . . .

Otherwise what you become is a bag full
of curdled cream—leche male, we call it—
attractive to nobody, least of all to
yourself!   Have you any plans?

KILROY: Well I was thinking   of going
on from here.

QUIXOTE: Good! Come with me!

Tennessee Williams, Camino Real

JUSTICIA EN MARCHA

La montaña de Llenares	G/D7

The mountain of Llenares
tiene corazón de plata.   C/D7/G
has a silver central heart
Teniendo al mexicano   D7
Holding down the Mexicano
a algunos les da plata.   G
a few get more than their part
Aqui vine porque vine
I came here because I came here
a llamar al mexicano   C/D7
to teach a little lesson
diciendo al que es ranchero   C/D7
to tell every Mexican field hand
que se porte muy tejano.   G
to start acting like a Texan

Por el camino que llevo
Down the road I travel
voy dejando yo mi lema:
I sow my little gem
levántese mexicano
stand up my Mexican brother
yo no quiero que usted tema.
Don't be afraid of them
Aquí vine porque vine
I came here beoause I came here
a venir a ver el valle
just to see the vale below
hay unos de una casita
but there are those in one little house there
que quieren quo yo me calle.
who wish that I'd go slow.

Song of the Texas Valley marchers, 1966, by
Father Antonio Gonzales 49S

GONNA SING MY LORD

Gonna sing my Lord   Am
for all that I'm worth   G/Am
Gonna sing my Lord   Dm
for all that I'm worth   C

Lord! Lord!   Em/Am
Gonna sing my Lord
for all that I'm worth   G/Am
Gonna sing my Lord   F
Lord! Lord!   Em/Am
till I see your face   Em/Am

Gonna live my Lord. . .
Gonna work my Lord. . .
Gonna love my Lord. . .

Song by Joe Wise 50

WE SHALL OVERCOME

We shall overcome   C/F/C
We shall overcome   F/C
We shall overcome someday C/Em/Am/D/G
Oh, deep in my heart   C/F/C
I do believe   F/G/Am
We shall overcome someday!   C/F/C/G/C

We are not afraid . . .
We are not alone . . .
We'll walk hand in hand . . .
The Lord will see us through . . .
We shall all be free . . .

Freedom Song 51

WOKE UP THIS MORNING

Woke up this morning   E
with my mind stayed on freedom
Woke up this morning   A7
with my mind stayed on freedom   E
Woke up this morning
with my mind stayed on freedom G#/C#m
Hallelu! Hallelu! Hallelujah!   E/B7/A7/E

And then! Walk! Walk!   E
And then! Talk! Talk!
with my mind on freedom!
And then! Walk! Walk!   A7
And then Talk! Talk!
with my mind on freedom!   E
And then Talk! Talk!

And then Walk! Walk!
with my mind on freedom   G#/C#m
Hallelu! Hallelu! Hallelujah!   E/B7/A7/E

Ain't no harm to keep your mind
stayed on freedom . . .

Walkin' and a talkin' with my mind
stayed on freedom . . .

Singin' and workin' with my mind
stayed on freedom . . .

Freedom Song [52s]

ODDS

The white man made the mistake of letting me read his history books. He made the mistake of teaching me that Patrick Henry was a patriot. . . . They didn't care about odds. They faced the wrath of the entire British Empire. . . . These thirteen scrawny states, tired of taxation without representation, tired of being exploited and oppressed and degraded, told that big British Empire, "Liberty or Death." And here you got twenty-two million Afro-Americans catching more hell than Patrick Henry ever saw. . . .

You got a new generation of Black people in this country who don't care anything whatsoever about odds. They don't want to hear you ole Uncle Toms, Handkerchief Heads, talking about odds. If they gonna draft these young Black men, send them over to Korea or South Vietnam to face eight hundred million Chinese— if you're not afraid of those odds, then you shouldn't be afraid of these odds.

Malcolm X, in one of his last speeches

O FREEDOM

I had reasoned dis out in my mind: There was two things I had a right to, liberty or death; if I could not have one, I would have the other; for no man would take me alive. I would fight for my liberty as long as my strength lasted, and when de time come for me to go, de Lord would let dem take me.

Harriet Tubman

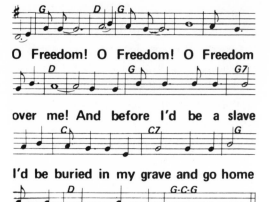

O Freedom! O Freedom! O Freedom
over me! And before I'd be a slave
I'd be buried in my grave and go home
to my Lord and be free!

No more conformin' . . .

Free to be honest . . .

Free to be me . . .

Free to build new things . . .

Adaptation of Freedom Song attributed originally to Negro Soldiers in the Civil War [53]

It'll be liberty or death, and if you're not ready to pay that price, don't use the word Freedom in your vocabulary.

Malcolm X

THE HELPING HAND

Perhaps you will say in your heart
"These nations are greater than I
How shall I ever displace them?"
But don't be afraid of them

Remember how the Lord your God
dealt with Pharaoh and all Egypt
the ordeals your own eyes have seen
his long arm and mighty hand

Deut. 7 in metrical chant [31]

THE WHOLE WORLD

He's got the whole world in his hands   c
He's got the big round world   G7
in his hands
He's got the whole world in his hands   c
He's got the whole world in his hands   G/C

He's got the tiny little baby in his hands

He's got you and me brother
in his hands . . .

He's got everybody in his hands . . .

Negro Spiritual [54]

WE SHALL NOT BE MOVED
FUERTES SOMOS YA

We shall not	G
we shall not be moved	D7
We shall not	
we shall not be moved	G
Just like a tree planted	C
by the water	G/Em
We shall not be moved	G/D7/G

Fuertes, fuertes, fuertes somos ya
Fuertes, fuertes, fuertes somos ya
como un árbol firme junto al río
Fuertes somos ya.

We're fighting for our freedom. . .
Luchamos por librarnos. . .

We're fighting for our children. . .
Luchamos por los hijos. . .

Coal Miners Song from West Virginia based on a hymn;
first sung in 1931.   Versión en espanol de Esther
Galli 55

> Let joy kill you.
> Keep away from
> the little deaths.
>
> Carl Sandburg

SEIZE JOY!

Reach out your hands	G
joy is passing by!	D7
Reach out your hands	
joy is passing by!	G
Reach out your hands	G7
joy is passing by!	C
Singin' glory hallelujah	G
joy is passing by!	D7/G

Take a chance on life
joy is passing by! . . .

Open up your mind . . .

Lift up your hearts . . .

The old world's a movin' . . .

A new world's comin' . . .

Wake up and live . . .

Adaptation of Negro Spiritual 56s

LA BAMBA

Para bailar la Bamba	B7/E/A/B7
To dance la Bamba	
Para bailar la Bamba	E/A/B7
To dance la Bamba	
Se necisita una poca de gracia	E/A/B7
All you need is a little bit of rhythm	
Una poca de gracia, y otra cosita	E/A/B7
A little bit of rhythm and a bit of soul	
Y arriba, y arriba	E
And up, and up	
Y arriba, y arriba, y arriba iré	A/B7
And up, and up, and up I'll go	
Por ti seré, por ti seré	E/A/B7
For you I'll be, for you I'll be	
Bamba, bamba	E/A/B7
Bamba, Bamba	E/A/B7
Bamba, Bamba	E/A/B7

Y no soy marinero
I'm not a sailor
soy capitán, soy capitán
I'm a captain, I'm a captain
Bamba Bamba Bamba Bamba
Bamba Bamba

Hang on Sloopy, Sloopy hang on! . . .

Twist and shout, twist and shout! . . .

A Mexican song with an infinite number of verses and
variations, so make up your own 57s

SEEK AND YOU SHALL FIND

Seek and you shall find	C
Knock and the door will open	F
Ask and it shall be given	Em
and his love comes a tumblin' down!	G7/C

Open your heart my brother. . .

Follow your star my brother . . .

Keep on a movin' brother . . .

Adaptation of White Spiritual 58s

THE CONFIDENCE CURE

I happened to notice you had this inferiority complex that keeps you from feeling comfortable with people. Somebody needs to build your confidence up and

make you proud instead of shy and
turning away and blushing.

Somebody —ought to —ought to —
kiss you, Laura!

Tennessee Williams, Glass Menagerie

GET TOGETHER

Love is but the song we sing   E
and fear's the way we die   D
You can make the mountain's ring   E
or make the angels cry   D
Know the dove is on the wing   E
and you need know not why   D

Come on people, now   A
smile on your brother   B
Let's get together   E
start to love one another   A/B7
right now   E

Some will come and some will go
and we shall surely pass
when the one who left us here
returns for us at last

We are but a moment's sunlight
fading in the grass
Come on people . . .

We can love our brothers now
though they are black or white
We can love our brothers now
though they are yellow or red
It makes no difference what color he is
just so a man's a man
Come on people . . .

If you've heard the song I sing
then you must understand
You hold the key to love and fear
all in your trembling hand
One key unlocks them both you know
and it's at your command
Come on people . . .

Song by Chet Powers [60]

I want you to know that because I knew I would find I feared to look into your eyes be- reflected there a merciless in- dictment of my impotence, and the compelling challenge to redeem my conquered manhood. My queen, it is hard for me to tell you what is in my heart for you today, what is in the heart of all my Black brothers for you and all your Black sisters, and I fear I will fail unless you reach out to me with the antenna of your love which you were unable to give me because I, being dead, was un worthy to receive it. But put on your crown, my queen, and we will build a new city on these ruins! — Eldridge Cleaver

Love

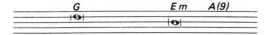

GROOM: As a lily among *thorns,* so is my

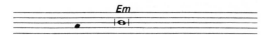

beloved a*mong* women

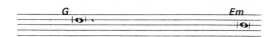

BRIDE: As an apple tree among the *trees*

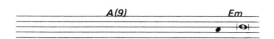

of the woods, so is my lover a*mong* men

Groom: Ah, you are beautiful, my be-
loved, Ah, you *are* beautiful!

Your eyes are doves be*hind* your veil.
You are beautiful, my beloved, and there
is no blem*ish* in you.

Bride: More delightful is your *love* than
wine! Your name spoken is a spread*ing*
perfume.

That is why the maidens *love* you. Bring
me, O king to *your chambers.*

Chorus: With you we rejoice and exult,
we ex*tol* your love; it is beyond wine;
how rightly you *are* loved.

Groom: How beautiful is your love, my
*sis*ter, my bride; how much more delightful is your love than wine, and the
fragrance of your ointment than *all*
spices!

You are an enclosed garden, my *sis*ter
my bride; you are a garden fountain,
a well of water, flowing fresh *from*
Lebanon!

Arise north wind! Come *south* wind!
Blow upon my garden that its perfumes
may spread *a*broad.

Bride: My lover speaks; he *says* to me
"Arise, my beloved, my beautiful one
and come."

For see, the winter is past, the rains are
*o*ver and gone. The flowers appear on
the earth, the time of pruning the vines
has come, and the song of the dove is
heard in our land.

My lover belongs to me and *I* to him.
Let me see you, let me hear *your* voice.

Groom: How beautiful you *are,* how
pleasing, my love, my *de*light

And your mouth like an excellent *wine—*

Bride: —that flows smoothly for *my*
lover.

I belong to my *lover,* and for me *he*
yearns

Chorus: For stern as death is *love,* relent-
less as the nether world is *de*votion.

Its flames are a blazing *fire* deep waters
cannot quench love, nor can floods
sweep it *a*way.

Canticles 1, 2, 4, 7, 8 modern chant 61

THE WORD I

GUTMAN: The word was spoken. The
crowd is agitated . . .

JACQUES: He said "Hermano." That's
the word for brother.

GUTMAN: Yes, the most dangerous
word in any human tongue is the word
brother. It's inflammatory. . . . It must
be reserved for strictly private usage in
back of soundproof walls. Otherwise it
disturbs the population.

JACQUES: The people need the word.

They're thirsty for it!
GUTMAN: What . . . these creatures?
Mendicants. Prostitutes. Thieves and
petty vendors in a bazaar where the
human heart is a part of the bargain.
JACQUES: Because they need the word
and the word is forbidden . . . .
GUTMAN: The word is said in pulpits
and at tables of council where its volatile
essence can be contained. But on the
lips of these creatures, what is it? A
wanton incitement to riot, without understanding. For what is a brother to
them . . . someone to get ahead of, to
cheat, to lie to, to undersell in the mar-
ket. Brother, you say to a man whose
wife you sleep with!—But now, you see,
the word has disturbed the people and
made it necessary to invoke martial law!

Tennessee Williams, Camino Real

THE WORD II

Throngs of people, obviously muslims
from everywhere bound on the pilgrim-
age, were hugging and embracing. They
were of all complexions, the whole at-
mosphere was of warmth and friendli-
ness. The feeling hit me that there really
wasn't any color problem here. The
effect was as though I had just stepped
out of prison.

Malcolm X

Say the word and you'll be free	A7
Say the word and be like me	
Say the word I'm thinkin' of	D7
Have you heard the word is love!	A7
It's so fine	E
It's sunshine	D7
It's the word: love!	A7

In the beginning I misunderstood
but now I've got it the word is good!
Say the word . . .

Everywhere I go I hear it said
in the good and the bad books
that I have read
Say the word . . .

Now that I know it
I feel I must be right,

I'm here to show everybody the light!

Give the word a chance to say
that the word is just a way
It's the word I'm thinkin' of
and the only word is love
So fine.
It's sunshine
Say the word, love!
Say the word, love!
Say the word, love!
Say the word, love!

Song by John Lennon and Paul McCartney 4

SHARING OF BREAD

Let us break the bread the
Lord has given us. Let all who
are hungry join us and eat.
Let all who are thirsty come
in and celebrate with us. This
year there are still men in
slavery. Next year, may all
men be free!

*Adaptation of opening prayer of the
Passover.*

RAMBLIN' BOY

He was a man	A/Bm
and a friend always	E/A
We rambled round	Bm
in the hard ol' days	E/A
He never cared if I had no dough.	D/A
We rambled round	Bm
in the rain and snow	E/A
So here's to you	A
my ramblin' boy	D
May all your rambles	B7/E
bring you joy	A
So here's to you	
my ramblin' boy	D/A
May all your rambles	Bm/E
bring you joy	A

In Tulsa town we chanced to stray
We thought we'd try to work one day
The boss says he had room for one.
Says my old pal,"We'd rather bum."
So here's to you my ramblin' boy . . .

Late one night in a jungle camp
the weather it was cold and damp
He got the chills, and he got them bad
They took the only friend I had
So here's to you my ramblin' boy . . .

He left me there to ramble on
My ramblin' pal is dead and gone
If when we die we go somewhere
I'll bet you a dollar he's ramblin' there
So here's to you my ramblin' boy . . .

Song by Tom Paxton [62]

THE WORD III

Love loves to love love
Nurse loves the new chemist
Constable 14A loves Mary Kelly
Gerty MacDonald loves
the boy that has the bicycle
M. B. loves a fair gentleman
Li Chi Hau lovey up kissy Cha Pu Chow
Jumbo the elephant loves
Alice the elephant
Old Mr. Verschoyle
with the ear trumpet
loves old Mrs. Verschoyle
with the turned in eye
The man in the brown macintosh
loves a lady who is dead
His Majesty the King loves
Her Majesty the Queen
Mrs. Norman W. Tupper
loves Officer Taylor
You love a certain person
and this person
loves that other person
because everybody loves somebody
but God loves everybody

James Joyce, Ulysses

ALL MIXED UP

You know this language	G
that we speak	D7
is part German	
part Latin and part Greek	G
with some Celtic and Arabic	
all in a heap	D7
well amended	
by the man in the street	G

Choctaw gave us	
the word "Okay"	C/G
"Vamoose" is a word	D
from Mexico way	G
And all of this is a hint	C/G
I suspect	
of what comes next	D7/G
I think that this whole world	C/D7/C
soon is gonna be get mixed up	D7/C
I think that this whole world	D7/C
soon is gonna be get mixed up	D7/C

I like polish sausage I like Spanish rice
Pizza pie is also nice
Corn and beans from the Indians here
washed down by some German beer
Marco Polo travelled by camel and pony
brought to Italy the first macaroni
And you and I as well as we're able
put it all on the table
I think that this whole world. . .

There were no redheaded Irishmen
before the Vikings landed in Ireland
How many Romans had dark curly hair
before they brought slaves from Africa?
No race of man is completely pure
nor is any man's mind and that's for sure
The winds mix the dust of every land
and so will man
I think that this whole world. . .

This doesn't mean
we will all be the same
We'll have different faces
and different names
Long live many different kinds of races
And its difference of opinion
that makes horse races
Just remember the rule
about rules, brother:
"What's right with one
is wrong with another"
And take a tip from La Belle France:
"Viva la Difference"
I think that this whole world. . .

Song by Pete Seeger [63]

GLORY

They make a life without glory. Instead of the heart they got the deep freeze in the house. The men, they don't feel no glory, not in the house with them women; they go to the bars, fight . . . get drunk, get fat, put horns on the woman because the woman don't give them the love which is glory. I did, I give him the glory. To me the big bed was beautiful like a religion.

Tennessee Williams, Rose Tattoo

WEDLOCK

A man was not created	G/C/Em/G
to walk this earth alone	C/D7
By God's design, a woman	G/C/Em/G
was formed from Adam's bone.	C/D7

GROOM
Flesh of my flesh	G/Em
Bone of my bone	C/D7
You are my loving bride.	C/D7/G

BRIDE:
I'm part of you	G/Em
I yearn for you	C/D7
My place is at your side	C/D7/G

This woman she was taken
from near to Adam's heart
by which we are reminded
that they should never part [Refrains]

This woman she was taken
from near to Adam's arm
and she must be protected
from injury and harm [Refrains]

This woman was not taken
from under Adam's feet
Because she shares his freedom
her gift of love is sweet   [Refrains]

This woman was not taken
from Adam's head we see
so she should not seek to rule him
but follow faithfully [Refrains]

Just as a loving husband
united with his wife
the Lord so loves his people
and shares with them his life [Refrains]

Just like the bride responding
to her true love's caress
in pleasing God his people
will find their happiness [Refrains]

Adaptation of White Spiritual [64s]

We're lonely. We're frightened...so now and then, although we've wounded each other time and again, we stretch out hands to each other in the dark that we can't escape from. We huddle together for some dim communal comfort, and that's what passes for love on this terminal stretch of the road . . . .

What is it, this feeling between us? When you feel my exhausted weight against your shoulder —when I clasp your anxious old hawk's head to my breast —what is it we feel in whatever is left of our hearts? Something, yes . . . delicate, unreal, bloodless! The sort of violets that could grow on the moon, or in the crevices of those far away mountains, fertilized by the droppings of carrion birds . . .

JACQUES: The violets in the mountains can break the rocks if you believe in them and allow them to grow!

Tennessee Williams, Camino Real

IF I HAD A HAMMER

If I had a hammer	C/Em
I'd hammer in the morning	F/G/C/Em/F
I'd hammer in the evening	G/C/Em/F
all over this land	G
I'd hammer out danger	C
I'd hammer out warning	Am
I'd hammer out love between	F/C
my brothers and my sisters	F/C
all over this land!	F/C/G/C/Em/F/G

If I had a bell
I'd ring it in the morning . . .

If I had a song . . .

Well we've got a hammer
and we got a bell
and we got a song to sing
all over this land

It's the hammer of justice
It's the bell of freedom
It's the song about love between
my brothers and my sisters
all over this land.

Song by Lee Hayes and Pete Seeger [66]

PRAYER FOR BROTHERHOOD

L: Have we not all one Father? Has not one God created us? Why then do we break faith with one another?

A: How good and pleasant for brothers to dwell together in unity. Here it is that the Lord has given us his blessing of eternal life.

L: You have been told what is good. What does the Lord require of you?

A: To do justice, to love kindness, and to walk humbly with God.

L: In days to come the Lord's house will rise, towering above every mountain.

A: They shall beat their swords into plowshares and their spears into pruning hooks.

L: Nation shall not lift up sword against nation. No longer shall men learn to fight.

A: Then the wolf shall lie down with the lamb, and the leopard will rest with the kid. None shall injure. None shall kill. For the land will be full of the knowledge of the Lord.

Adaptation of Jewish prayer

LAY DOWN MY SWORD AND SHIELD

I'm gonna lay down   G
my sword and shield
down by the riverside!
down by the riverside!   D7
down by the riverside!   G
I'm gonna lay down
my sword and shield
down by the riverside
down by the riverside!   D7/G

I ain't gonna study war no more!   C
I ain't gonna study war no more!   G
I ain't gonna study war no more!   D7/G

I ain't gonna study war no more!   C
I ain't gonna study war no more!   G/Em
I ain't gonna study war no more!   D7/G

I'm gonna put on my Freedom Robe . . .

I'm gonna lay down my threats
and frowns . . .

I'm gonna put on my happy face . . .

I'm gonna make love and give up war . . .

Adaptation of Negro Spiritual [67]

A GOLDEN THREAD

Oh had I a golden thread   G/C
and needle so fine   G/D
I'd weave a magic strand   G/C
of rainbow design   G/D7
of rainbow design   C/G/D7/G

In it I'd weave the bravery
of women giving birth
In it I would weave the innocence
of children over all the earth
children of all earth

Far over the water
I'd reach my magic band
through foreign cities
to every single land
to every land

Show my brothers and my sisters
my rainbow design
Bind up this sorry world
with hand and heart and mind
hand and heart and mind

Far over the waters
I'd reach my magic band
to every human being
so they would understand
so they'd understand

Song by Peter Seeger [68]

EXPORT YOUR REVOLUTION
OR IT DIES ON THE VINE!
IS IT GOOD? GIVE IT AWAY!

Daniel Berrigan

Love that is hoarded molds in time

until we learn some day the only things

we ever keep are what we give away

Love is like a song

Floating on the air

It's *not* **meant** *for* **your** *pock*et

It's *meant* **for** *all* **to** *share*

Love that is too careful
turned in and alone
will slowly dry and harden
until its like a stone
Love that is hoarded . . .

Love is like a banquet
spread for all mankind
Join with all your neighbors
Don't be left behind
Love that is hoarded . . .

Chant adaptation of early American folk hymn 69

Sorrow

THE LONELINESS OF CAPTIVITY

MOTHERLESS CHILD

Sometimes I feel	Em-A
like a motherless child	C/B7/Em
Sometimes I feel	Am7-Bm7
like a motherless child	Gmaj7/B7/Em-A
Sometimes I feel	
like a motherless child	C/B7/Em
A long way from home	Am7/B7/Am7/Em
A long way from home	Am7/B7/Em-A

Sometimes I feel like I have no friend. . .

Sometimes I feel like I never been born.

Sometimes I feel like I'm almost dead. . .

Negro Spiritual 70

NO MAN IS AN ISLAND

No man is an island
entire to himself
Everyman is a piece of the continent
a part of the main
If a clod of earth
be washed away by the sea
Europe is the less
as well as if a whole promontory were
as well as if the house of a friend
or of thine own were
Any man's death diminishes me
because I am involved in mankind
So therefore never send to know
for whom the bell tolls
it tolls for thee

John Donne

ELEANOR RIGBY

I look at all the lonely people	F/Am
I look at all the lonely people	F/Am
Eleanor Rigby picks up the rice	Am
in a church	D
where a wedding has been	Dm
Lives in a dream	Am
Waits at the window, wearing the face	
that she keeps	D

in a jar by the door	Dm
Who is it for?	F/Am
All the lonely people	F
where do they all come from?	Am
All the lonely people	F
where do they all belong?	Am

Father McKenzie, writing the words
of a sermon that no one will hear
No one comes near
Look at him working
darning his socks in the night
when there's nobody there
What does he care?

All the lonely people
where do they all come from?
All the lonely people
where do they all belong?

I look at all the lonely people
I look at all the lonely people

Eleanor Rigby died in the church
and was buried along with her name
Nobody came
Father McKenzie, wiping the dirt
from his hands
as he walks from the grave
No one was saved

All the lonely people
where do they all come from?
All the lonely people
where do they all belong?

Song by John Lennon and Paul McCartney 4

SOLITARY CONFINEMENT

And so we talk to each other, write and
wire each other, call each other short
and long distance across land and sea,
clasp hands with each other at meeting
and at parting, fight . . . and even
destroy each other because of this always somewhat thwarted effort to break

through walls to each other. As a character in a play once said, "We're all of us
sentenced to solitary confinement inside
our own skins."

Tennessee Williams, The Timeless World of a Play

MIDNIGHT SPECIAL

Well, you wake up in the morning	C6
hear the ding-dong ring	G6
You go a-marching to the table	Em/D7
see the same damn thing	G
Well, it's on-a one table	C6/Cmaj7
knife, a fork and a pan	C6/Cmaj7/G6
And if you say anything about it	D7
You're in trouble with the man	G

Let the midnight special	C6
shine her light on me	G6
Let the mignight special	D7
shine her everloving light on me	C/D7/G

If you go to Houston
you better walk right
You better not stagger
you better not fight
Sheriff Benson will arrest you
he'll carry you down
And if the jury finds you guilty
penitentiary bound
Let the midnight special . . .

Yonder comes my woman
How'n the world do you know
Well, I know her by her apron
and the dress she wore
Umbrella on her shoulder
piece of paper in her hand
Goes a-marching to the captain
say "I want my man"
Let the midnight special . . .

I'm going away to leave you
and my time ain't long
The man is going to call me
and I'm going home
Then I'll be done my grieving
whooping, hollering and crying
I'll be done my studying
about my great long time
Let the midnight special . . .

Prison song 71

RICHARD CORY

Whenever Richard Cory went downtown
we people on the pavement
looked at him
He was a gentleman from sole to crown
clean-favored and imperially slim.
And he was always quietly arrayed
and he was always human
when he talked.
But still he fluttered pulses when he said
"Good morning"
and he glittered when he walked.
And he was rich—yes, richer than a king—
and admirably schooled in every grace.
In fine, we thought that he was everything
to make us wish that we were in his place.
So on we worked, and waited for the light
and went without the meat
and cursed the bread.
And Richard Cory
one calm summer night
went home and put a bullet
through his head.

Edwin Arlington Robinson

INQUEST

About 9:19 P.M., Monday, May 1, 1967,
while in the rear of the Benning Post
Office, 3900 Block, Minnesota Avenue,
S.E. Washington, D.C., and while strug-
gling with his prisoner in an attempt to
maintain his arrest, the service revolver
of Private W.L.R., white, male, 22 years,
of 532 Landry Lane, Oxon Hill, Mary-
land, a Colt .38 caliber, serial # 834-825
discharged, striking his prisoner, C.J.B.,
Negro, male, 19 years, of 266 Kennil-
worth Terrace, N.E. Washington, D.C.

There was a gunshot entrance wound on
the skin of the back of the body. . .the
skin around the bullet wound was clean
and showed no smoke or effects of gun-
powder or anything of that sort. . . .The
bullet passed through the lower lobe of
the right lung and there was a big hole in
the lung from which a lot of blood had
flowed. . . .The cause of death was gunshot wound of the back and the right
lung. . . .

Excerps from record of a Coroner's Inquest

JOHNNY, I HARDLY KNEW YE

Where are the legs   Em
When Johnny comes
with which you run
marching home again
Hurroo! Hurroo!   G/D
Hurrah, hurrah!
Where are the legs   Em
We'll give him
with which you run
a hearty welcome, then
Hurroo! Hurroo!   G/B7
Hurrah, hurrah!
Where are the legs   Em
The men will cheer
with which you run   D
the boys will shout
When you went to carry a gun   Em/B7
The ladies, they will all turn out
Indeed, your dancing days   Em/D/C
And we'll all
are done   D
feel gay
Och, Johnny, I hardly knew ye.   B7/Em
when Johnny comes marching home.

You haven't an arm
Get ready
and you haven't a leg
for the jubilee
Hurroo! Hurroo!
Hurrah, hurrah!
You haven't an arm
We'll give the hero
and you haven't a leg
three times three
Hurroo! Hurroo!
Hurrah, hurrah!
You haven't an arm
The laurel wreath
and you haven't a leg
is ready now
You're an eyeless, noseless
chickenless egg
To place upon his loyal brow
You'll have to be put with a bowl to beg
And we'll all feel gay
Och, Johnny, I hardly knew ye.
When Johnny comes marching home.

Irish song. It suffers in the American Translation 72

WHERE HAVE ALL THE FLOWERS GONE?

Now, when they were in the field, Cain turned against his brother and killed him. The Lord asked Cain, ''Where is your brother Abel?'' And Cain replied, ''I do not know. Am I my brother's guardian?''

Then the Lord exclaimed, ''What have you done? The voice of your brother's blood cries out to me from the ground! You are cursed by the soil which opened its mouth to receive your brother's blood. When you till the ground it will no longer yield its fruit to you. You are a fugitive outcast of the earth.   *Genesis 4*

Where have all the flowers gone   C
Long time passing   D7/G7
Where have all the flowers gone   C
Long time ago   F/G
Where have all the flowers gone   C
Young girls picked them everyone   D7/G7
When will they ever learn   F/G7/C
When will they ever learn?   F/G7/C

Where have all the young girls gone
. . . gone to young men everyone

Where have all the young men gone
. . . gone for soldiers everyone

Where have all the soldiers gone
. . . gone to graveyards everyone

Where have all the graveyards gone
. . . gone to flowers everyone

Song by Pete Seeger 75

O COME EMMANUEL

O Come, o come, Emmanuel   Dm/Gm/Dm
and ransom captive Israel   F/Bb/Am/Dm
that mourns in lonely exile here   Gm/Bb/F
until the Son of God appears   Dm/Gm/Dm

Rejoice! Rejoice! O Israel!   F/Dm/Gm/Dm
To you shall come Emmanuel   F/Bb/Am/Dm

O come, Desire of Nations, bind
in one the hearts of all mankind
O bid our sad divisions cease
and be for us our King of Peace

Adaptation to be sung in traditional style or in Samba arrangement of James Minchin 77

KILLING

. . . each man kills
the thing he loves
by each, let this be heard
Some do it with a bitter look
some with a flattering word
The coward does it with a kiss
the brave man with a sword

Some kill their love
when they are young
and some when they are old
Some strangle with the hands of lust
some with hands of gold
The kindest use a knife
because the dead so soon
grow cold

Oscar Wilde, Ballad of Reading Gaol

CLEANSE ME

Guilt towers over my head
Its weight is too heavy to bear
My wounds are foul and festering
the result of my own folly

Friends shrink from my wounds
Those closest to me keep their distance
Others threaten me with ruin
plotting against me all day

Cleanse me and wash me, Lord
Blot out all my guilt
Put some joy and gladness into my life
In the secret of my heart
teach me wisdom

Psalms 38 and 51 in metrical chant [31]

ATONEMENT

This, rather, is the fasting that I wish:
releasing those unjustly bound, untying
the thongs of the yoke, setting free the
oppressed, breaking every yoke, sharing
your bread with the hungry, sheltering
the oppressed and the homeless, clothing
the naked, and not turning your *back*
on your own kin.

Then your light will shine like the dawn
and your wound *will* be quickly healed.

Isaiah 58 in Gregorian chant [1]

When so many seem to be
lonely, it would be inexcusably
selfish to be lonely alone.

Tennessee Williams, Camino Real

BREAK BREAD TOGETHER

Let us break bread	D
together with the Lord!	Em/D
Let us break bread	D
together with the Lord!	Em/D
As we travel through this land	D7
with our brothers hand-in-hand	G/Em
O Lord fill our livin'	D/A7
with your life!	D/G/D

Let us drink wine together with the Lord

Let us sing songs together. . .

Let us make this a new world. . .

Adaptation of Negro Spiritual [78s]

PRAYER

God bless all the cats without pads in the
Plaza tonight.

God bless all con men and hustlers and
pitch men who hawk their hearts on the
street; all two time losers who are likely
to lose once more; the courtesan who
made the mistake of love; . . . the
poet who wandered far from his heart's
green country and possibly will and
possibly won't be able to find his
way back.   Look down with a smile
tonight on the last Cavaliers, the ones
with rusty armour and soiled white
plumes; . . . visit with understanding and
something that's almost tender those
fading legends that come and go in the
Plaza like songs not clearly remembered.
And, sometime and somewhere, let there
be something to mean the word honor
again.

Amen.

Tennessee Williams, Camino Real

OUR FATHER

Our Father	E/Bm7
who art in heaven	E/Bm7
Hallowed be thy name!	E/Bm7/E
Thy kingdom come	Bm7/E/F#m
Thy will be done	G#m/A

Hallowed be thy name!
On earth, as it is in heaven
Hallowed be thy name!
Give us this day, our daily bread
Hallowed be thy name!
And forgive us all of our trespasses
Hallowed be thy name!
As we forgive those
who trespass against us
Hallowed be thy name!
And lead us not
unto the devil to be tempted
Hallowed be thy name!
But deliver us from all that is evil
Hallowed be thy name!
For thine is the kingdom
and the power and the glory
Hallowed be thy name!
Forever and ever
and ever and ever
Hallowed be thy name!

West Indies Melody [79]

WE CAN WORK IT OUT

Try to see it my way	A
Do I have to keep on talkin'	G
'till I can't go on?	D/A
While you see it your way	
run the risk of	
knowing that our love	G/D
will soon be gone	A
We can work it out	D/A
We can work it out	D/E

Think of what you're saying
You can get it wrong
and still you think that
it's all right
Think of what I'm saying
we can get it straight
and work it out
or say good night

We can work it out
We can work it out

Life is very short	F#m
and there's no time	Bm/C#
for fussing and fighting my friend	F#m
I have always thought	
that it's a crime	Bm/C#
so I will ask you once again	F#m

Try to see it my way
only time will tell
if I am right or I am wrong
While you see it your way
there's a chance that we
might fall apart before too long
We can work it out. . .

Song by John Lennon and Paul McCartney [4]

Father deLeo, you love your people but you don't understand them. They find God in each other and when they lose each other, they lose God and they are lost. And it's hard to help them.

Tennessee Williams, The Rose Tattoo

AWAY OVER YONDER

Let us send men ahead to explore the land and report to us on the road we must follow and the cities we must take. They set out and explored and reported "The land which the Lord our God gives us is good."

Deut. 7

My brother's gone	C/Em7
to view the land	F/C
My brother's gone	Em7/Dm7
to view the land	G7
My brother's gone	C/C7
to view the land	Fmaj7/Dm7
and wear a starry crown	Fmaj7/G7/C
Away over yonder	Dm7
Away over yonder	Fmaj7/G7
Away over yonder	C/C7
and wear a starry crown	Fmaj7/G7/C

My father's gone to view the land

My mother's gone to view the land . . .

White Spiritual [80s]

GUANTANAMERA

Guantanamera   G
guajira guantanamera   A/D/Em/A
Guantanamera   D/G/A
guijira guantanamera   D/G/A
Guantanamera   G
guijira guantanamera   A/D/Em/A
Guantanamera   D/G/A
guijira guantanamera   D/G/A

Yo soy un hombre sincero   A/D/G
I am a truthful man
de donde crece la palma   A/D/G/A
from the land of the palm tree
Yo soy un hombre sincero   A/D/G
I am a truthful man
de donde crece la palma   A/G/A
from the land of the palm tree
Antes de morirme   A/D
And before I die
quiero echar mis   G/A
I would like to share
versos del alma   D/G/A
my verses with you
Guantanamera . . .

Mi verso es de un verde claro
My verses are a clear green
de un carmín encendido
and they are flaming crimson
Mi verso es de un verde claro
My verses are a clear green
y de un carmín encendido
and they are flaming crimson
Mi verso es un ciervo herido
My verses are a wounded fawn

que busca en el monte amparo
seeking the refuge of the forest
Guantanamera . . .

Con los pobres de la tierra
With the poor people of the earth
quiero yo mi suerte echar
I will cast my lot
Con los pobres de la tierra
With the poor people of the earth
quiero yo mi suerte echar
I will cast my lot
El arroyo de la sierra
The streams of the mountain
me complace más que el mar
are more pleasing to me than the sea
Guantananmera . . .

*José Martí's love song to the poor people of Cuba
—the "guajira"— the outcasts who lived in the bush
("girl from Guantanamo") who harvested the sugar
cane for the rich Spaniards who lived in the cities
by the sea.[82]*

DEEP RIVER

Of death the Negro showed little fear,
but talked of it familiarly and even
fondly as simply a crossing of the waters
perhaps —who knows?— back to his
ancient forests again.

W.E.B.DuBois, The Souls of Black Folk

Deep river   D/Bm
my home is over Jordan   G/Em/F#m
Deep river, Lord   D/Bm
I want to cross over   G/Em
to my homeland   D

O don't you want to go   G/Em/F#m
to that Gospel feast   G/Em/D
that promised land   G/Em/F#m
where all is peace?   Em/A
Deep river . . .

Negro Spiritual [83s]

Let his going from us serve only to bring us together—now. Consign these immortal
remains to earth, the common mother of all, secure in the knowledge that what we
place in the ground is no more now a man, but a seed, which after the winter of our
discontent will come forth again to meet us, and we will know him then for what he
was and is—a prince—our own Black Prince, who didn't hesitate to die because
he loves us so.

Ossie Davis at funeral of Malcolm X

Change

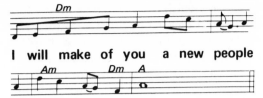

I will make of you a new people

Dm / Am / Dm / A

A people full of joy!
If you remove oppression
from your midst
false accusations and malicious speech
If you share your bread
with the hungry
and help the afflicted

Then light will shine for you
in the darkness and the gloom
will become bright as midday

Isaiah 58 in metrical chant 31
*Antiphon based on Isaiah 65 by M. J. Archer
and A. D. Rosetti* 84

A NEW DAY

I can see a new day   *C/G7*
a new day soon to be   *C*
when the storm clouds
are all past   *F*
and the sun shines   *C*
on a world that is free   *G7/C*

I can see a new world
a new world coming fast
when all men are brothers
and hatred forgotten at last

I can see a new man
a new man standing tall
with his head high
and his heart proud
and afraid of nothing at all

Song by Les Rice 85

WAYFARING STRANGER

The Lord said to Abram: "Leave your
country, your kinfolk and your father's
house for the land which I will show
you."

Genesis 12

THE ROAD OF PROMISE

I'm just a poor   *Dm*
wayfaring stranger
travelin' through   *Gm*
this world of woe   *Dm*
where men don't trust   *A7*
don't know their savior   *Dm*
don't know the love   *Gm*
to which they're called   ⌐ *Dm*

I'm heading there   *Bb*
to live in glory   *A7*
to feel the trust   *Bb*
which brothers know   *A7*
I'm moving in   *Dm*
the spirit of oneness
I'm travelin on   *Gm*
the glory road   *Dm*

I know dark clouds
will gather round me
I know my way is steep and rough
but fields of peace
of living in freedom
are just ahead—we see them now
I'm heading there . . .

I want to be in the new world
that's bornin'
To have those fields
possessed by sons
I want to work
in the fragrance of freedom
I want to live with brothers as one
I'm heading there . . .

Adaptation of White Spiritual by John Snyder 86s

LONESOME TRAVELER

VAL: You might think there's many
and many kinds of people in this world
but, Lady, there's just two kinds of
people, the ones that are bought and the
buyers. No! There's one other kind. . .
The kind that's never been branded.

LADY: You will be, man.

VAL: They got to catch me first.

LADY: Well, then, you better not settle
down in this county.

VAL: You know they's a kind of bird that don't have legs so it can't light on nothing . . . has to stay all its life on its wings in the sky?. . . You can't tell these birds from the sky and that's why the hawks don't catch them up there in the high blue sky near the sun!. . . They live their whole lives on the wing, and they sleep on the wind. . . They just spread their wings and go to sleep on the wind like other birds fold their wings and go to sleep on the tree. . . . They sleep on the wind and never light on this earth but one time when they die!

LADY: I'd like to be one of those birds.

VAL: So'd I like to be one of those birds. They's lots of people would like to be one of those birds.

Tennessee Williams, Orpheus Descending

I am a lonely	
and a lonesome traveler	*Dm*
I am a lonely	
and a lonesome traveler	*G*
I am a lonely	*Dm*
and a lonesome traveler	*(F/Bb)*
And I'm travelin' on	*Dm*
	Bb/A/Dm

I traveled cold and then
I traveled hungry. . .

I travel with the rich man
and with the poor man. . .

Gonna keep on a travelin'
on the road to freedom. . .

American Folk Song [87S]

THE GOLDEN APPLES

You know the tale, –how swarthy Atlanta, tall and wild, would marry only him who outraced her; and how the wily Hippomenes laid three apples of gold in the way. . . .

Atlanta is not the first or the last maiden whom greed of gold has led to defile the temple of Love; and not maids alone, but men in the race of life, sink from the high and generous ideals of youth to the gambler's code of the Bourse; and in all our Nation's striving is not the Gospel of Work befouled by the Gospel of Pay? So common is this that one-half think it normal; so unquestioned, that we almost fear to question if the end of racing is

not gold, if the aim of man is not rightly to be rich. . .

Work and wealth are the mighty levers to lift this old new land; thrift and toil and saving are the highways to new hopes and new possibilities; and yet the warning is needed lest the wily Hippomenes tempt Atlanta to think that golden apples are the goal of racing and not mere incidents by the way.

W.E.B. DuBois, The Souls of Black Folk

I DON'T WANT YOUR MILLIONS MISTER

I don't want	*Am*
your millions mister	*G/Am*
I don't want	*Dm*
your diamond ring	*C/Em*
All I want	*Am*
is the right to live mister	*G/Am*
Give me a job	*Dm*
that fits a man	*F/Am*

I don't want your Rolls-Royce, mister
I don't want your pleasure yacht
All I want is food for my babies
Give me a job that fits a man

We worked to build this country, mister
While you enjoyed a life of ease
You've stolen all that we built, mister
Now our children starve and freeze

Think me dumb if you wish, mister
Call me green, or blue, or red
This one thing I sure know, mister
My hungry babies must be fed.

Adaptation of Jim Garland's adaptation of "East Virginia" in 1932 Coal mining wars in Harlan County, Kentucky [88S]

IDOLS OF SILVER AND GOLD

We have come to regard the Kremlin as the permanent seat of the devil's power, and have grown almost comfortable with a menace which, though unspeakably evil, has had the redeeming virtues of constancy, predictability, and familiarity. Now the devil has betrayed us by traveling abroad. . .turning up now here, now there, and in many places at once with a devilish disregard for the laboriously constructed frontiers of ideology.

We are confronted with a complex and fluid world situation and we are not adapting ourselves to it. We are clinging to old myths in the face of new realities, and we are seeking to escape the contradictions by narrowing the permissible bounds of public discussion, by relegating an increasing number of ideas and viewpoints to a growing category of "unthinkable thoughts."

Senator J. William Fulbright, March 25, 1964

To the Lord alone	G/C
give glory	G/D7
not to idols	
of silver and gold	D6/D7/G
not to us	
or the things we make	C/G/D7
idols of silver and gold	D6/D7/G

For they have eyes	Dm/G7/C
but they cannot see	
and they have ears	Dm/Eb/G
but they cannot hear	
and they have noses	D7/G/D7
but they cannot smell	
they're the work	
of human hands!	D6/D7/G
And they have mouths	Dm/G7/C
but they cannot speak	
and they have hands	Dm/Eb/G
but they cannot feel	
and they have feet	D7/G/D7
but they cannot walk	
their makers	
will become like them!	D6/D7/G

Old myths
that we learned in school
idols of silver and gold!
New schemes
that just came in style
idols of silver and gold!
For they have. . .

The way we always do things
idols of silver and gold!
The program we've just designed
idols of silver and gold!
For they have. . .

Song based on Psalm 115 89S

A NEW SONG

In every generation a man must regard himself as though it were he personally who came out of Egypt: As it is written

"And you will tell your son on that day, saying: This is because of that which the Lord did for me, when I came out of Egypt." Not only our fathers did the Holy One deliver, but he also delivered us, and our children, and our children's children from generation to generation. Therefore it is our duty to thank, praise, and honor him who did all these wonders for our fathers and for us. He brought us from slavery to freedom, from sorrow to joy, from mourning to rejoicing, from darkness to great light, from captivity to redemption. Let us therefore sing to him a new song!

Now come on	E/B7/E
Sing to the Lord a new song!	A/B7/A
Sing to the Lord all nations!	E/A/E
Sing to the Lord	B7
and praise his name!	B6/B7/E/B7/E

Now come on
Sing to the Lord a new song!
Sing to the Lord all nations!
Sing to the Lord
and praise his name!

For the innocent	E
the dawn of hope	
Let the rivers clap their hands	B7/E
Dawn of gladness	
for honest hearts	
Let the mountains shout for joy	B7/E
Now come on. . . .	

Let the sea and its creatures roar
Let the rivers clap their hands
Let the heavens be glad and rejoice
Let the mountains shout for joy
Now come on. . . .

We'll sing praise to the Lord
with the harp
Let the rivers clap their hands
And with trumpets
and the sound of the horn
Let the mountains shout for joy
Now come on. . . .

Adaptation of prayer from Passover Ritual and song based on Psalms 95-99 90S

A NEW LIFE

Humanity shows itself in all its intellectual splendor during this tender age as the sun shows itself at the dawn, and the flower in the first unfolding of the petals; and we must respect religiously, reverently these first indications of individuality.

If any educational act is to be efficacious, it will be only that which tends to help toward the complete unfolding of this life. To be thus helpful it is necessary rigorously to avoid the arrest of spontaneous movements and the imposition of arbitrary tasks.

Maria Montessori

WHAT DID YOU LEARN IN SCHOOL TODAY

What did you learn in school today   *E/A/E*
dear little boy of mine?   *B7*
What did you learn in school today   *E/A/E*
dear little boy of mine?   *B7*
I learned that Washington   *A*
never told a lie   *E*
I learned that soldiers seldom die   *A/E*
I learned that everybody's free   *A/E*
That's what the teacher said to me   *A/E*
And that's what I learned in school today
That's what I learned in school   *A/B7/E*

What did you learn in school today. . .
I learned that policemen are my friends
I learned that justice never ends
I learned that murderers
die for their crimes
even if we make a mistake sometimes
And that's what I learned in school today
That's what I learned in school. . .

I learned our government must be strong
It's always right and never wrong
Our leaders are the finest men
and we elect them again and again
And that's what I learned in school today
That's what I learned in school. . .

I learned the wars are not so bad
I learned about the great ones
that we have had
We fought in Germany and in France
And someday I might get my chance
And that's what I learned in school today
That's what I learned in school. . .

Song by Tom Paxton[91]

My atheism, like that of Spinoza, is true piety towards the universe and denies only gods fashioned by men in their own image, to be servants of their human interests; and that even in this denial I am no rude iconoclast, but full of secret sympathy with the impulses of idolaters.

George Santayana, Soliloquies in England

SIMPLE GIFTS

It's a gift to be simple   G
It's a gift to be free
It's a gift to come down   D7
where we ought to be
And when we see ourselves   G
in a way that's right
we will live   D7
in a valley of love and delight!   G
When true simplicity is gained
to live and to love
we will not be ashamed   D7
To laugh and to sing   G
will be our delight
Till by laughing and singing   D7
we come 'round right!   G

The earth is the Lord's
and the fullness thereof
Its streets, its slums
as well as stars above
Salvation is here
where we laugh, where we cry
where we seek and love
and live and die

When true liberty is found
by fear and by hate
we will then not be bound
In love and in life
we will find a new birth
In peace and in freedom
redeem the earth

It's a gift to be simple. . .

Adaptation of Shaker Hymn 92S

REVENGE

Lord, God of Revenge, appear
rise up and judge the world
Give to the proud their just deserts
How much longer
are the wicked to triumph?

Are these evil men to go unpunished
boasting and asserting themselves?
Lord, they crush your people
murdering and slaughtering
widows and orphans

Psalm 94 in metrical chant [31]

SOMEBODY'S KNOCKIN' AT YOUR DOOR

Somebody's knockin'   *C/F/Cetc.*
at your door
Somebody's knockin'
at your door   *G7/Dm7/G7etc.*
O Mourner!   *C/F/Cetc.*
Why don't you answer?
Somebody's knockin'
at your door   *G7/C/Fetc.*

Sounds like a new world callin'
Somebody's knockin' at your door
Sounds like a new world callin'
Somebody's knockin' at your door
O Mourner! Why don't you answer?
Somebody's knockin' at your door

Adaptation of Negro Spiritual [93s]

LAW AND ORDER I

Bolshevism is knocking at our gates. We
can't afford to let it in. We have got to
organize ourselves against it, and put our
shoulders together and hold fast. We
must keep America whole and safe and
unspoiled. We must keep the worker
away from red literature and red ruses;
we must see that his mind remains
healthy.

Al Capone

THE DEVIL WORE A CRUCIFIX

The Devil wore a crucifix   *Dm/A*
"The Christians they are right"   *Dm/A*
the Devil said   *Dm*
"So let us burn   *Gm*
a heretic tonight"   *Dm/A/Dm*
a heretic tonight!   *Dm/A/Dm*

A lily or a swastika
a shamrock or a star
the devil he can wear them all
no matter what they are
no matter what they are!

Whenever there's a lynching
the Devil will be there
A witch or an apostle
the Devil doesn't care
the Devil doesn't care!

He'll beat a drum in China
He'll beat it in the west
He'll beat a drum for anyone
A holy war is best
A holy war is best!

Song by Sydney Carter [94]

TEAR DOWN THE IDOLS

"When the Lord, your God, brings you
into the land which you are to enter and
occupy, and dislodges great nations before you, tear down their altars, smash
their sacred pillars, chop down their
sacred poles, and destroy their idols by
fire. For you are a people sacred *to* the
Lord, your God.

Deut. 7 in Gregorian Chant [1]

TA—RA—RA—RA—BOOM—DEE—AY

I had a job once threshing wheat   *C*
worked sixteen hours
with hands and feet
and when the moon
was shining bright   *G7*
they kept me working all the night   *C*
One moonlight night I hate to tell
I accidentally slipped and fell
My pitchfork went right in between   *G7*
some cogwheels of
the thresh machine   *C*

TA RA RA BOOM DEE AY
It made a noise that way
and wheels and bolts and hay   *G7*
went flying every way   *C*
That stingy rube said "Well
a thousand shot to Hell"
But I did sleep that night   *G7*
I needed it all right   *C*

Next day the stingy rube did say
"I'll bring my eggs to town today
You grease my wagon up you mutt
and don't forget to screw the nut"
I greased his wagon all right but
I plumb forgot to screw that nut
and when he started on that trip
the wheel slipped off and broke his hip

TA RA RA BOOM DEE AY
It made a noise that way
That rube was sure a sight
and mad enough to fight
His whiskers and his legs
were full of scrambled eggs
I told him "That's too bad
I'm feeling very sad"

And then that farmer said
"You Turk, I bet you are
an 'I Won't Work' "
He paid me off right there by gum
So I went home and told my chum
Next day when threshing did commence
My chum was Johnny on the Fence
and 'pon my word that awkward kid
he dropped his pitchfork like I did

TA RA RA BOOM DEE AY
It made a noise that way
and part of that machine
hit Reuben on the bean
He cried "Oh Me! Oh My!
I nearly lost an eye"
My partner said "You're right
It's bed time, now good night"

Song by Joe Hill [95]

LAW AND ORDER II

If civil authorities pass laws or command
anything opposed to the moral order and
consequently contrary to the will of
God, neither the laws made nor the
authorization granted can be binding on
the consciences of the citizen since God
has more right to be obeyed than men.

If any government does not acknowledge
the rights of man or violates them, it not
only fails in its duty, but its orders completely lack juridical force.

Pope John XXIII, Pacem In Terris

ARISE!

Brothers and sisters	G
why crouch ye like cravens	
to clutch at existence	D7/G
of insult and want?	D7
Why stand to be plucked	G
by an army of ravens	
or hoodwinked forever	D7
by promise and talk	G
Think on the wrongs you bear!	D7
Think on the rags you wear!	G
Think on the insults	D7/G
endured from your birth!	D7
Toiling in snow and rain!	G
Piling up heaps of gain!	
All for the tyrants	D7
that grind ye to earth!	G

Your brains are as keen
as the brains of your masters
In swiftness and strength
you surpass them by far
Your brave hearts have taught you
to laugh at disasters
Your children deserve more
than slavery and chains
Why then like cowards stand
using not brain nor hand
thankful like dogs
when they throw you a bone!
What right have they to take
things that you toil to make?
Know ye not brothers
that all is our own?

Arise in our might brothers
bear it no longer
Assemble our people
through all the land
We'll show these blood suckers
who are the stronger
when workers stand up
to the robber band
Waste not your ready blows
Seek not for foreign foes
Your bitterest enemy
treads your own soil
The sweaters that grind you
the ranters that blind you
the gluttons that revel
while you are at toil

Jim Connell's words to O'Donnell Abu [96s]

300 YEARS

And the only point I'm trying to make is
this, man, I'm a Vet. I need a place to
live, and I don't have no time to fool
around with Chuck over a place to live.

I'm workin' and I need a home. I don't have time to explain to him why I'm black, you see—I don't have time to do that. I don't have time to explain to him why people out here broke these windows three or four weeks ago—I don't have time to explain that to him you see The sucker knows but he wants you to stop and explain it to him. You can't explain these things partner. It's a lot deeper than Black power—any kind of power—It's something we have suffered for over 300 years—you see.   This is something we have fought and suffered over 300 years.

Transcription of a Rap & Suds Session
Build Black, Inc., Washington, D.C., April, 1968 [47]

SAMSON

Read about Samson   *D/G/D etc.*
from his birth
the strongest man
that ever lived on earth
Read away down in ancient times
he killed three thousand Philistines

If I had my way   *D/C*
If I had my way   *G/D*
If I had my way   *F#m/Bm*
I would tear this building down! *E/A/D/G/D*

They bound him with a rope and
while walking along
he looked down and saw an old jawbone
He moved his arms
the rope snap like thread
When he got through movin'
three thousand was dead

If I had my way. . .

Delilah was a woman fine and fair
very pleasant lookin' and coal-black hair
Delilah, she gained old Samson's mind
when he saw the woman
and she looked so fine

If I had my way. . .

They shaved his hair
like the palm of his hand
and his strength
became like a nachul' man
Took po' Samson to the judgment hall
bound him and chained him
against the wall

If I had my way. . .

He called a little boy
about three feet tall
says "Place my hands
up against the wall"
And he tore that building down!

He said "And now I got my way
and now I got my way
and now I got my way"
And he tore that building down!

Negro Spiritual [97]

LAW AND ORDER III

Judges like Brandeis, Cardozo, Hughes, Murphy, Stone and Rutledge brought to the bench a libertarian philosophy and used it to shape the law to the needs of an oncoming generation. In that sense they were "activists," criticized by many. But history will honor them for their creative work. They knew that all life is change and that law must be constantly renewed if the pressures of society are not to build up to violence and revolt.

Justice William O. Douglas, An Almanac of Liberty

BURN BABY BURN

"Is God dead?"
Sojourner Truth's question electrified the audience. Frederick Douglass replies, "No, God is not dead, and therefore slavery must end in blood."

Middle of the summer   *F#m/E/F#m, etc.*
bitten by flies and fleas
sittin' in a crowded apartment
about a hundred and ten degrees

I went outside
the middle of the night
All I had was a match in my hand
but I wanted to fight

So I said a burn baby burn
Burn baby burn
Nowhere to be, no one to see
I said a nowhere to turn   C#m/B7
Burn baby burn   E

I heard people talking
about a dream, now
a dream I couldn't catch
I really wanted to be somebody
and all I had was a match
Couldn't get oil from Rockefeller's wells
Couldn't get diamonds from the mine
If I can't enjoy the American Dream
won't be water but fire next time
So I said. . .

Walkin' around the west side now
lookin' mean and mad
Deep down inside my heart
I'm feeling sorry and sad
Got a knife and a razor blade
everybody that I know is tough
But when I burned my way
out of the ghetto
I burned my own self up
when I said. . .

Learn, baby, learn
learn, baby learn
You need a concern
You've got money to earn
You've got midnight oil to
burn, baby, burn

I really want a decent education
I really want a decent place to stay
I really want some decent clothes, now
I really want a decent family
I really want a decent life
like everybody else

Song by Jimmy Collier 98

VELVET VIOLENCE I

A developed person conceals and compli-
cates his inner states of evil. [In
relations with children] anger and pride

fuse together in a complex whole which
assumes that precise, quiet, and respectable shape known as tyranny.
Only as the child grows older does he
begin to direct his reactions against
tyranny; but then the adult finds reasons
to justify himself and to entrench himself still more firmly behind his camou-
flage. Sometimes he even succeeds in
convincing the child that such tyranny
is for his good.

"Respect" is paid by one side only; the
weak respecting the strong.

It is thought legitimate for the adult to
offend the child. He can judge the child,
or speak ill of him, and does it openly,
even going so far as to strike him. . . .A
protest from the child is considered as
insubordination that it would be dangerous to tolerate.

Maria Montessori, The Secret of Childhood

RESPECT

What you want   C
Baby I've got it   F/G7
What you need   etc.
you know I've got it
All I'm asking
is for a little respect
Just a little bit
just a little bit
Just a little bit
just a little bit

I ain't gonna do you wrong
tie you down
I ain't gonna do you wrong
cause I don't want to
All I'm asking
is for a little respect

Song by Otis Redding as sung by Aretha Franklin 99

SHE'S LEAVING HOME

Wednesday morning at five o'clock   A/D
as the day begins   F#m/B
silently closing the bedroom door   Bm/E
leaving a note that she hoped   Bm/E
would say more
she goes downstairs to the kitchen   A/D

clutching her handkerchief   *F#m/B*
quietly turning the back door key   *Bm/E*
stepping outside she is free   *Bm/E*

She   *A*
(We gave her most of our lives)
is leaving
(Sacrificed most of our lives)
home
(We gave her everything   *C#m*
money could buy)   *F#m*
She's leaving home
after living alone   *B*
for so many years   *F#m*

Father snores as his wife
gets into her dressing gown
picks up the letter that's lying there
Standing alone
at the top of the stairs
she breaks down
and cries to her husband
"Daddy, our baby's gone
Why would she treat us
so thoughtlessly!
How could she do this to me!"

She (we never thought of ourselves)
is leaving
(never a thought for ourselves)
home (we struggled hard
all our lives to get by)
She's leaving home
after living alone for so many years
Bye, bye

Friday morning at nine o'clock
she is far away
waiting to keep
the appointment she made
meeting a man
from the motor trade

She (what did we do
that was wrong)
is having (we didn't know
it was wrong)
fun (fun is one thing
that money can't buy)
Something inside
that was always denied
for so many years (Bye bye)
She is leaving home (Bye bye)

Song by John Lennon and Paul McCartney [4]

REVOLUTIONARY WORLD

The answer is to rely on youth —
not a time of life, but a state of mind
a temper of the will, a quality of imagin-
ation, a predominance of courage over
timidity, of the appetite for adventure
over the love of ease.

The cruelties and obstacles of this swift-
ly changing planet will not yield to
obsolete dogmas and outworn slogans.
They cannot be moved by those who
cling to a present that is already dying,
who prefer the illusion of security to the
excitement and danger that come with
even the most peaceful progress.
It is a revolutionary world we are
living in.

Robert F. Kennedy

TURN, TURN, TURN

To ev'rything   *C*
(Turn, turn, turn)   *F/Em/Dm*
There is a season   *C*
(Turn, turn, turn)   *F/Em/Dm*
And a time   *G7*
For every purpose
under heaven   *C*

A time to be born   *C/G7*
a time to die   *C*
a time to plant   *G7*
a time to reap   *C*
a time to kill   *G7*
a time to heal   *C*
a time to laugh   *F*
a time to weep   *G7/C*
To ev'rything. . .

A time to build up
a time to break down
a time to dance, a time to mourn
a time to cast away stones
a time to gather stones together
To ev'rything. . .

A time of war, a time of peace
a time of love, a time of hate
a time you may embrace
a time to refrain from embracing
To ev'rything. . .

Words from Ecclesiastes 3 adapted to music by Pete Seeger [100]

A NEW GENERATION

I think there's a need to change the environment. The young generation is escaping from it with pot and acid; the older generation is taking pills, tranquilizers, and alcohol to cool its nerves. People would be a lot less frigid and hung up if they designed their surroundings so they could enjoy them more, so that they could be turned on by them.

Diana Dew, Designer of the "Electric Dress"

I'M ON MY WAY

I'm on my way (I'm on my way)	*E*
to the Freedom land	*B7*
(to the Freedom land)	
I'm on my way (I'm on my way)	
to the Freedom land	*E*
(to the Freedom land)	
I'm on my way (I'm on my way)	*E7*
to Freedom land (to Freedom land)	*A*
I'm on my way, Great God	*E/B7*
I'm on my way	*E*

I'll ask my brother
to come go with me. . .

If he can't go
I'm gonna go anyhow. . .

If you can't go
don't hinder me. . .

Freedom Song 101S

Struggle

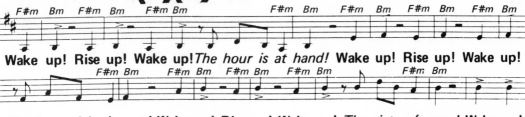

Wake up! Rise up! Wake up! *The hour is at hand!* **Wake up! Rise up! Wake up!**

The long night is past! **Wake up! Rise up! Wake up!** *The victory's near!* **Wake up!**

Rise up! Wake up! Rise up! Wake up! Rise up!

Wake up! Rise up!
Wake up! *A new day is here!*
Wake up! Rise up!
Wake up! *Come out of the dark!*
Wake up! Rise up!
Wake up! *Come out of the past!*
Wake up! Rise up! Wake up! Rise up!
Wake up! Rise up!

. . . Come out in the light!
. . . To stand up and fight!
. . . To fight for what's right!

. . . The poor from the dust!
. . . The sick from despair!
. . . The cities in ruin!

Covey at length let me go, puffing and blowing at a great rate, saying that if I had not resisted, he would not have whipped me half so much. The truth was, that he had not whipped me at all. I considered him as getting entirely the worst end of the bargain; for he had drawn no blood from me, but I had from him. The whole six months afterwards, that I spent with Mr. Covey, he never laid the weight of his finger upon me.

This battle with Mr. Covey was the turning-point in my career as a slave. It rekindled the few expiring embers of freedom, and revived within me a sense of my own manhood.

It was a glorious resurrection, from the tomb of slavery, to the heaven of freedom.

Frederick Douglass

IT ISN'T NICE

It isn't nice to block the doorways   D/Bm
It isn't nice to go to jail   G/A
There are nicer ways to do it   D/Bm
but the nice ways always fail   G/A
"It isn't nice! It isn't nice!"   D/Bm
You told us once   G
you told us twice   A7
but if that's freedom's price   G/A
we don't mind   D

It isn't nice to carry banners
or to sleep in on the floor
or to shout our cry of freedom
at the hotel and the store
"It isn't nice! It isn't nice!"
You told us once, you told us twice
but if that's freedom's price
we don't mind

Well, we've tried negotiations
and the three-man picket line
Mr. Charlie didn't see us
and he might as well be blind
Now our new ways aren't so nice
when we deal with men of ice
but if that's freedom's price
we don't mind

How about those years of lynchings
and the shot in Evers' back?
Did you say it wasn't proper?
Did you stand out on the track?
You were quiet just like mice
now you say we aren't nice
but if that's freedom's price
we don't mind

Song by Malvina Reynolds 102

JESUS CHRIST

The instinct of nearly all societies is to lock up anybody who is truly free. First, society begins by trying to beat you up. If this fails, they try to poison you. If this fails too, they finish by loading honors on your head.

Jean Cocteau

Jesus Christ was a man	*G*
that travelled through the land	*C/G*
hard working man and brave	*D7*
He said to the rich	*G*
give your goods to the poor	*C/G*
so they laid Jesus Christ	*D7*
in his grave	*G*

Jesus was a man	*C*
a carpenter by hand	*G*
his followers true and brave	*D7*
One dirty little coward	*G*
was hired for the job	*C*
and they laid Jesus Christ	*G/D7*
in his grave	*G*

He went to the sick
he went to the poor
and he went to the hungry
and the lame
Said that the poor
would one day win this world
and so they laid Jesus Christ
in his grave
Jesus was a man. . .

He went to the preacher
he went to the sheriff
told them all the same
sell all your jewelry
and give it to the poor
but they laid Jesus Christ
in his grave
Jesus was a man. . .

When Jesus came to town
the working folks around
believed what he did say
the bankers and the preachers
they nailed him on a cross
and they laid Jesus Christ
in his grave
Jesus was a man. . .

When the love of the poor
shall one day turn to hate
when the patience
of the workers gives way
"Would be better for you rich
if you never had been born"
so they laid Jesus Christ
in his grave
Jesus was a man. . .

This song was written
in New York City
of rich men, preachers, and slaves
Yes, if Jesus was to preach
like he preached in Galilee
they would lay Jesus Christ
in his grave
Jesus was a man. . .

Woodie Guthrie's words to tune of "Jesse James" 103

BATTLE HYMN OF THE REPUBLIC

Mine eyes have seen the glory	*G*
of the coming of the Lord	*G7*
He is trampling out the vintage	*C*
where the grapes of wrath	*G*
are stored	
He has loosed the fateful lightning	
of his terrible swift sword	*B7/Em*
His truth is marching on	*Am/G/D/G*
Glory, glory, hallelujah	*G/G7*
Glory, glory, hallelujah	*C/G*
Glory, glory, hallelujah	*Em/B7/Em*
His truth is marching on	*Am/G/D/G*

He hath sounded forth the trumpet
that shall never call retreat
He is sifting out the hearts of men
before his judgment seat
O be swift my soul to answer him
be jubilant my feet
Our God is marching on
Glory, glory, hallelujah. . .

In the beauty of the lilies
Christ was born across the sea
with a glory in his bosom
that transfigures you and me
As he died to make men holy
let us live to make men free
while God is marching on
Glory, glory, hallelujah. . .

Julia Ward Howe and William Staffa

To survive inside this hell hole we must begin to teach love and respect for each other and stop fighting and cutting each other. . . .Whenever black people get together, white people condemn that unity. Unless we unite, we won't be saved.

Stokely Carmichael

SOLIDARITY FOREVER

Solidarity forever
Solidarity forever
Solidarity forever
For the union makes us strong

When the union's inspiration
through the worker's blood shall run
There can be no power greater
anywhere beneath the sun
Yet what force on earth is weaker
than the feeble strength of one
For the union makes us strong
Solidarity forever. . .

In our hands is placed a power
greater than their hoarded gold
Greater than the might of armies
magnified a thousand fold
We can bring to birth a new world
from the ashes of the old
For the union makes us strong

Union variation of Battle Hymn of the Republic by Ralph Chaplin, 1915

SOLIDARIDAD POR SIEMPRE

Solidaridad por siempre
Solidaridad por siempre
Solidaridad por siempre
Con la fuerza sindical

Llevaremos en la sangre
la grandeza sindical
No tendra poder mas grande
el laborismo mundial
Companero, si eres debil
con tu fuerza individual
Busca la unidad gremial

Mas que el oro atesorado
es el poder sindical
Es mas fuerte que una armada
y mejor que un arsenal
Crearemos nueva vida
en el campo laboral
Con la fuerza sindical

Spanish variation of union variation

PRAYER OF STEEL

Lay me on an anvil, O God. Beat me into a crowbar. Let me pry loose old walls; let me lift and loosen old foundations.

Carl Sandburg

GLEE REIGNS IN GALILEE

Glee reigns in Galilee   Dm
the Galil rejoices
Brave hearts are singing, brothers
lift up your voices!

Through nights of witching darkness F
flutes softly sounding
the watchman of Galilee
his watchsong resounding   A
Glee reigns in Galilee. . .

Sing ho, my Galilee
O sing on my heart strings
Strong in my love for you
I fear not what fate brings
Glee reigns in Galilee. . .

Why skip like rams, you hills?
Like young lambs, you mountains?
Why does the sea run out?
The Jordan stop flowing?
Glee reigns in Galilee. . .

Who turns the solid rock
into pools of water?
Who turns the flinty ground
into flowing fountains?
Glee reigns in Galilee. . .

Tremble, O Earth
Here comes your Lord
and your Master
The God of Jacob's here
He lives in his people
Glee reigns in Galilee. . .

Israeli song, Gilu Hagalilim, with additional verses from Psalm 114 [104s]

ONE MAN'S HANDS

Democracy is a process, not a static condition. It is becoming, rather than being. It can easily be lost, but never is fully won. Its essence is eternal struggle.

William H. Hastie

One man's hands	C
can't tear a prison down	G7
Two man's hands	
can't tear a prison down	C
But if two and two and fifty	F
make a million	Em
We'll see that day come 'round	G/Am
We'll see that day come 'round	Dm/G7/C

One man's vote
can't make the Congress see. . .

One man's love
can't end this night of fear. . .

Song by Alex Comfort and Pete Seeger [105]

THE PARTNERSHIP

"Therefore, if you harken to my voice and keep my covenant, you shall be my special possession, dearer to me than all other people, though *all* the earth is mine.
"You shall be to me a kingdom of priests, a *holy* nation."

Exodus 19 in Gregorian Chant [1]

PROMISES TO KEEP

You tell me to slow down	G/A
I'm movin' too fast	D/Bm
"Take it easy"	G
and "rest for a while"	C/A

Why can't you see that	G/Gm
there's much more to be done	D/Bm
Why we've only covered the first mile	G/A
And I have promises to keep	D/Em/D
and miles to go before I sleep	Em/A
and miles to go before I sleep	G/A/D

You say that a job
well begun is half done
so you start
that's all the farther you go
Seems like we just
got started on this road
and now you're movin' so slow
But I have promises to keep. . .

If you don't see me
on your rutted down road
don't worry
I'm up ahead
Sorry I can't wait
for you anymore
Only hope
you'll follow my tread
For I have promises to keep . . .

Song by Ann Marie McLoone based on a phrase from a poem by Robert Frost [106s]

LIFT EVERY VOICE AND SING

Lift every voice and sing
till earth and heaven ring
ring with the harmonies of liberty
Let our rejoicing rise
high as the listening skies
Let it resound loud as the rolling sea

Sing a song full of faith
that the dark past has taught us
Sing a song full of hope
that the present has brought us
Facing the rising sun
of our new day begun
let us march on till victory is won

Stony the road we trod
bitter the chastening rod
felt in the days
when hope unborn had died
yet with a steady beat
have not our weary feet
come to the place
for which our fathers sighed?

We have come over a way
that with tears has been watered
We have come, treading our path
through the blood of the slaughtered
Out from the gloomy past
til now we stand at last
where the white gleam
of our bright star is cast

"The Negro National Anthem" by James Weldon Johnson and J. Rosamond Johnson [107]

If there is no struggle, there is no progress. Those who profess to favor freedom, and yet deprecate agitation, are men who want crops without plowing up the ground.

Frederick Douglass

GOD CALLED ADAM

God called Adam! Hallelujah!
God called Adam! Halleloo!
God called Adam! Hallelujah!
"To tend and rule my garden"

God called Noah! Hallelujah!
God called Noah! Halleloo!
God called Noah! Hallelujah!
"To build my children an ark"

God called Moses. . .
"To lead my people on"

God called John. . .
"To clear away the path"

God called Peter. . .
"To teach my people the way"

He's callin' you and me. . .
"To overcome evil with good"

Song by Mother Scott [108S]

√ WHEN I FIRST CAME TO THIS LAND

When I first came to this land	D/G/D
I was not a wealthy man	G/D/A7/D
So I got myself a shack	G/D
I did what I could	Em/A7/D
And I called my shack	G/D
"Break my back"	A7/D
But the land was sweet and good	G/D
And I did what I could	Em/A7/D

. . .cow
called my cow "No milk now"

. . .duck
called my duck "Out of luck"

. . .wife
called my wife "Run for your life"

. . .son
called my son "My work's done"

Pennsylvania Dutch Song arranged by Oscar Brand [109]

With a good conscience our only sure reward, with history the final judge of our deeds, let us go forth to lead the land we love, asking His blessing and His help, but knowing that here on earth, God's work must truly be our own.

John F. Kennedy

THE TEACHER'S LAMENT

Some people say	Em
a teacher's made out of steel	C7
Her mind can think	B7/Em
but her body can't feel	C7/B7
iron and steel and hickory tea	Em/Am
frowns and gripes	Em
from nine to three	Am/Em

You teach six full hours	Em
and what do you get?	C7/B7
Another day older	Em
and deeper in debt	C7/B7
You pay your dues	Em
in this and that	
Then for twenty-nine days	Am
your bill-fold's flat	Em

I woke one morning
it was cloudy and cool
I picked up my register
and started for school
I wrote eighty-four names
on the home room roll
And the Principal said
"Well, bless my soul"

You teach six full hours
and what do you get?
Cuts and bruises
and dirt and sweat

I got two black eyes
and can hardly walk
When I turned my back
then came the chalk

I got eighty-four kids
and forty-two seats
Sixty are talking
while twenty-four sleep
I can hardly get 'em all
through the classroom door
And if I don't watch out
they'll give me twenty-four more

You teach six full hours
to eighty-four brats
And all of them yelling
like dogs and cats
They're cutting on the seats
and writing on the walls
Hugging and kissing
in the upstairs halls

The last bell rings
and I start for the door
My head is ringing
And my feet are sore
I taught six full hours
my day is made
But I still have
three hundred papers to grade

You teach six full hours
and what do you get?
Another day older
and deeper in debt
I'll go to St. Peter
but I just can't stay
I gotta come back
to the P.T.A.

A teacher's adaptation of "Sixteen Tons" by Joe Glazer 110

FOREVER

The world grasps me
in hands that hurt
carries me to the fire
and burns me at the stake
I burn and I burn
and I'm not consumed
I rise up again and go on

I harness myself
in the gear of a horse
Over me a rider lashes in rage
I am driven like a plow
through the earth
I rise up again and go on

I live in a prison
I break open the door
The freed men trample me
in their rush to escape
They leave me lying
in blood on the floor
I rise up again and go on

My clothing bloody
my feet scarcely crawl
I come with love
of anguished yesterdays
I come to a hovel
on its steps I fall
I rise up again and go on

From a Yiddish poem by Halper Leivick

THE WEARIN' OF THE GREEN

O Paddy dear and did you hear   C
the news that's goin' round?   G7
The shamrock is forbid by law   F/C
to grow on Irish ground   G7/C
Saint Patrick's Day we'll keep no more
his colors can't be seen   G7
for there's a bloody law agin'   F/C
the wearin' of the green   G7/C

I met with Napper Tandy   F/C
and he took me by the hand
and he said "How's poor old Ireland   C
and how does she stand?"   G7
She's the most distressful country   C
that ever you did see   G7
They're hangin' men and women   F/C
for the wearin' of the green   G7/C

But if the color we must wear
is England's cruel red
let it remind us of the blood
that Ireland has shed
Then pull the shamrock from your hat
and throw it on the sod
and never fear 'twill take root there
tho' under foot 'tis trod

When law can stop the blades of grass
from growing as they grow
And when the leaves in summer time
their color dare not show
Then I will change the color too
I wear in my caubeen
But till that day, please God I'll stick
to wearin' of the green

Irish Street Song

Tyranny, like hell, is not easily conquered; yet we have this consolation
with us, that the harder the conflict, the
more glorious the triumph. What we
obtain too cheap, we esteem too lightly;
it is dearness only that gives everything
its value.   Heaven knows how to put a
proper price upon its goods; and it
would be strange indeed if so celestial
an article as freedom should not be
highly rated.

Thomas Paine

WHICH SIDE ARE YOU ON?

Which side are you on?	*Dm/A*
Which side are you on?	*Dm*
Which side are you on?	*A*
Which side are you on?	*Dm*

Come all of you good workers	*A*
good news to you I'll tell	*Dm/A/Dm*
of how the good old union	*A*
has come in here to dwell	*Dm/A/Dm*
Which side are you on. . .	

My daddy was a freedom fighter
and I'm a freedom son
I'll stick right with this struggle
until the battle's won
Which side are you on. . .

They say in Hinds county
no neutrals have they met
You're either for the freedom ride
or you tom for Ross Barnett
Which side are you on. . .

Don't scab for the bosses
Don't listen to their lies
Us poor folks haven't got a chance
unless we organize
Which side are you on . . .

*Song by Florence Reece written during the bloody
efforts to organize the miners of Harlan County in the
nineteen thirties, interspersed with adapted verses by
the Freedom Riders of the sixties* [111s]

THE MAN THAT WATERS THE WORKERS' BEER

I'm the man, the very fat man	*D*
that waters the workers' beer	*A7/D*
Yes, I'm the man, the very fat man	
that waters the workers' beer	*A/E7/A*
What do I care if it makes them ill?	*G*
Or it makes them terribly queer?	*D*
I've a car, a yacht	*A7/D*
and an aeroplane	
and I waters the workers' beer	*A7/D*

When I makes the workers' beer
I puts in strychinine
some methylated spirits
and a drop of paraffin
But since a brew so terribly strong
might make them terribly queer
I reaches my hand for the water tap
and I waters the workers' beer

A drop of good beer is good for a man
who's thirsty, tired, and hot
and sometimes I has a drop for myself
from a very special lot
But a fat and healthy working class
is the thing that I most fear
so I reaches my hand for the water tap
and I waters the workers' beer

Now ladies fair, beyond compare
be ye maid or wife
Oh, sometimes lend a thought for one
who leads a wand'ring life
The water rates are shockingly high
and chemicals are so dear
so there isn't the profit there used to be
when I waters the workers' beer

*Words by Paddy Ryan to "Son of a Gambolier,"
better known as the "Ramblin' Wreck"* [112]

I never did give anybody hell. I just told the truth and they thought it was hell.

Harry S. Truman

PITY THE DOWNTRODDEN LANDLORD

Please open your hearts	F/Bb
and your purses to a man	F/F7/Bb
who is misunderstood	Bbm/F
He gets all the kicks	A/A7
and the curses	Dm
though he wishes	G
you nothing but good	G7/C7
He wistfully begs you	F/Bb
to show him you think	F/F7/Bb
he's a friend not a louse	Bbm/F
so remember the debt	F#dim
that you owe him	C
the landlord	C#dim/Dm7
who lends you his house	G7/C7

So pity the downtrodden landlord	F/Bb/F
and his back	F7/Bb
that is burdened and bent	Bbm/F
Respect his gray hairs	F#dim/Gm
don't ask for repairs	C7/F
and don't be behind	Gm/C7
with the rent	F

When thunderclouds gather and darken
You can sleep undisturbed in your bed
But the landlord must sit up and hearken
And shiver, and wonder and dread
If you're killed, then you die in a hurry
And you never will know your bad luck
But the landlord is shaking with worry
"Has one of my houses been struck?"
So pity the downtrodden. . .

When a landlord resorts to eviction
Don't think he does it for spite
He is acting from deepest conviction
And what's right, after all, is what's right
But I see that your hearts
are all hardened
And I fear I'm appealing in vain
Yet I hope my last plea will be pardoned
If I beg on my knees once again
So pity the downtrodden. . .

Song by B. Woolf and Arnold Clayton. A song which originated in England during World War II. The melody approximates "She's More to Be Pitied than Censured." 113

PRAYER

Ever insurgent let me be
Make me more daring than devout
From slick contentment keep me free
And fill me with a buoyant doubt

Louis Untermeyer

PUT IT ON THE GROUND

Oh, if you want a raise in pay	F
all you have to do	G7
Go and ask the boss for it	C7
and he will give it to you	F
Yes, he will give it to you, my boy	
he will give it to you	G7
A raise in pay without delay	C7
Oh, he will give it to you	F

Oh, put it on the ground	C7/F
spread it all around	G7
Dig it with a hoe	C7
it will make your flowers grow	F

For men who own the industries
I'm sheddin' bitter tears
They haven't made a single dime
in over thirty years
in over thirty years, my boy
in over thirty years
Not one thin dime in all that time
in over thirty years
Oh, put it on the ground. . .

Union Song by Ray Glaser and Bill Wolf 114

EVERYBODY LOVES SATURDAY NIGHT

Bobo waro fero Satodeh	G/D7/G
Bobo waro fero Satodeh	D7/G
Bobo waro Bobo waro	D7
Bobo waro Bobo waro	G/D7
Bobo waro fero Satodeh	G/D7/G

Everybody loves Saturday night
Everybody loves Saturday night
Everybody, everybody
Everybody, everybody
Everybody loves Saturday night

Tout le monde aime Samedi soir
Tout le monde aime Samedi soir
Tout le monde, tout le monde
Tout le monde, tout le monde
Tout le monde aime Samedi soir
(French)

Jeder eyne hot lieb Shabas ba nacht
Jeder eyne hot lieb Shabas ba nacht
Jeder eyne hot, jeder eyne hot
Jeder eyne hot, jeder eyne hot
Jeder eyne hot lieb Shabas ba nacht
(Yiddish)

Nigerian Humor vs. British Curfew [115]

FREEDOM NOW

I said now — nanananananana. . .
Freedom now — nanananananana. . .
Freedom now — nanananananana. . .

Do you want your freedom?	Oh yes
Do you want it now?	Oh yes
Do you want your freedom?	Oh yes
Come on and sing it now	Oh yes
Do you want your freedom?	Oh yes
I said now — nanananananana. . .	

Do you want a good job?	Oh yes
Then join the movement	Oh yes
Do you want education?	Oh yes
Then come with me	Oh yes
Then we're gonna march	Oh yes
I said now — nanananananana. . .	

Make up your own verses

New words by the Chicago Movement to Wilson Pickett's Land of a Thousand Dances

JOSHUA

Now the trumpet summons us again — not as a call to bear arms, though arms we need — not as a call to battle, though in battle we are — but a call to bear the burden of a long twilight struggle year in and year out. "Rejoicing in hope, patient in tribulation" — a struggle against the common enemies of man: tyranny, poverty, disease and war itself.

John F. Kennedy

Joshua fit the battle of Jericho   Dm
Jericho, Jericho   A7/Dm
Joshua fit the battle of Jericho
and the walls   A7
come a tumblin' down   Dm

Up to the walls of Jericho   Dm
he marched with spear in hand
"Go blow them horns" Joshua cried
"cause the battle is in my hands"   A7/Dm
Joshua fought the battle of Jericho. . .

Then the lamb, ram, sheep horns
begin to blow, trumpets begin to sound
Joshua commanded
the children to shout
and the walls
come a tumblin' down

Slavery's chains are broke at last
broke at last, broke at last
Slavery's chains are broke at last
and the walls
come a tumblin' down

I know my Jesus helped me
cause his spirit spoke to me
said, "Rise up all my brothers
and you too shall be free"
Slavery's chains are broke at last. . .

Negro Spiritual [116]

AMAZING LOVE

A man that's wild is hard for a woman to hold, huh? But if he was tamed — would the woman want to hold him?

Tennessee Williams, Rose Tattoo

Amazing love has banished fear   E/A/E
and conquered death with life   B
I once was blind, but now I see   E/A/E
true love is kissed by strife   B/E

Amazing love has shown the way
to fields so fresh and free
I once was lost but now I've found
that life can bloom for me

Adaptation of White Spiritual [117S]

Help

HELP

Help—I need somebody	Bm
Help—Not just anybody	G
Help—You know I need someone	E
Help	A

When I was younger	D
so much younger than today	F#m/Bm
I never needed anybody's	
help in any way	C/G/D
And now those days are gone	D
I'm not so self assured	F#m/Bm
Now I find I've changed my mind	
I've opened up the door	C/G/D

Help me if you can, I'm feelin' down	Em
And I do appreciate your bein' round	C
Help me get my feet	A
back on the ground	
Won't you please, please help me	D/C/Bm

And now my life has changed
in oh so many ways
My independence seems to
vanish in the haze
But every now and then
I feel so insecure
I know that I will lead the life
I've never done before

Help me if you can. . .

Help me! Help me!

Song by John Lennon and Paul McCartney 4

Changes in outer or inner environment may demand degrees of freedom not permitted by the existing structure and may necessitate its partial and/or temporary disintegration, in the same way that growth necessitates the periodical shedding of the shell in crustacea and other arthropods. This act of demolishing carefully erected structures, though indispensible if better adapted ones are to arise, is always followed by a period of dangerous vulnerability, as is impressively illustrated by the defenseless situation of the newly moulted crab.

Konrad Lorenz

BLIND MAN
STOOD IN THE ROAD AND CRIED

Been travelin' round	Dm/C
a jumbled up world	Bb/A7
It's hard to see	Dm
what I see	A7
People aren't movin'	Dm/C
just driftin' around	Bb/A7
Don't know what they	Dm
want to be	A7

The blind man stood in	Dm/C
the road and cried	Bb/A7
The blind man stood in	Dm/C
the road and cried	Bb/A7
The blind man stood in	Dm/C
the road and cried	Bb/A7
Crying ohhh . . .	G/F/E
Show me the way	A/G/F/E

Places are changin'
when man meets man
My spot is different
each day
One man moves up
another moves down
Where will I be
tomorrow?
The blind man . . .

There's war, there's peace
no difference in between
The battle of words
goes on
If the fighting stops
we cut each other down
keeping men apart
and alone
The blind man . . .

There's GTO's
there's LSD
USA, USSR
VIP
There's so many things
making us who
we can't afford
to be
The blind man . . .

Adaptation of Negro Spiritual 118

THIRSTY BOOTS

True freedom is to share all the chains
our brothers wear and with heart and
hand to be earnest to make others free.

James Russell Lowell

You've long been on	C/G
the open road	Am
you've been sleeping	F
in the rain	G
From the dirt of words	C/G
and the mud of cells	Am
your clothes are smeared	F
and stained	G
But the dirty words	C/G
the muddy cells	Am
will soon be judged insane	F/G
So only stop and rest yourself	C/F/C
till you are off again	F/Dm/G
Then take off your thirsty boots	C/F
and stay for a while	C/F
Your feet are hot and weary	C/Am
from a dusty mile	F/G
And maybe I can make you laugh	C/F
maybe if I try	C/F
Just lookin' for the evenin'	C/Am
and the mornin' in your eyes	Dm/G7/C

But tell me of the ones you saw
as far as you could see
across the plain from field to town
a-marching to be free
and of the rusted prison gates
that tumbled by degree
like laughing children, one by one
who looked like you and me.
Then take off your thirsty boots . . .

I know you are no stranger
down the crooked rainbow trails
from dancing cliff-edged shattered sills
of slander shackled jails
but the voices drift up from below
as the walls they're being scaled
all of this and more, my friend
your song shall not be failed
Then take off your thirsty boots . . .

Song by Eric Anderson [119]

He gives others confidence. With him
I think I could do anything.

Jacqueline Kennedy

FREEDOM
IS A CONSTANT STRUGGLE

They say that Freedom	Am
is a constant struggle	E/Am
They say that Freedom	Dm
is a constant struggle	E/Am
They say that Freedom	
is a constant struggle	E/Am
O Lord, we've struggled so long	Dm
We must be Free!	Am
We must be Free!	E/Am

They say that Freedom
is a constant sorrow
. . .
O Lord we've sorrowed so long
We must be Free!
We must be Free!

They say that Freedom
is a constant crying
. . .
O Lord we've cried so long
We must be Free!
We must be Free!

They say that Freedom
is a constant dying
. . .
O Lord we've died so long
We must be Free!
We must be Free!

They say that Freedom
is a constant struggle . . .

Freedom Song [120]

STRENGTH

Strengthen the hands that are feeble
Make firm the knees that are weak
Say to those whose hearts are frightened
"Be strong and do not fear"

"Be strong and do not fear
Here your God is with you

Divine vengeance is coming
Retribution is coming to save you."

Then the eyes of the blind will be opened
and the ears of the deaf shall hear
The lame shall leap like a deer
and the tongues of the dumb sing for joy.

Isaiah 35 in metrical chant [31]

COME BY HERE

So Officer R. walks up to this cat they call Fat Nasty. And so he tell Fat Nasty he's under arrest for stealing. So Fat Nasty start beating his hands together like this, saying, "you ain't taking me nowhere man." So the police look like he was scared. . . . So, in the process, when the police walked up to Fat Nasty, he had dropped a box of cookies and something else. So Clarence picked the cookies up and said,"Fat Nasty, do you want your cookies?" So he said, "No man, ain't got time for these cookies."

So Clarence put the cookies back down on the ground. And the police said, "You are under arrest for throwing trash on the ground." So he left Fat Nasty alone and came over and grabbed Clarence by the arm. And so we wondered why he'd leave Fat Nasty alone— he stole something—and that he would get the man for throwing cookies on the ground. . . .

So I told Clarence to run. So the Officer pulled out his gun. By the time his gun got to around about this high, Clarence grabbed his hand. So they started wrestling with the gun. So I told him to run. So he say, "Catfish"—that's what they call me, "Catfish," you know—so he say, "Catfish, help me!" And I told him there wasn't nothing I could do, just let the gun go and run. So, I don't think the police would shoot him for putting cookies down on the ground. So he let the gun go and he started to run. And the Police shot him. . . .

Testimony of Rufus "Catfish" Mayfield at Coroner's Inquest

Come by here, my Lord   C
come by here   F/C

Come by here, my Lord   Em
come by here   F/G7
Come by here, my Lord   C
come by here   F/C
O Lord, come by here   F/C/G7/C

We need Justice, Lord, come by here
We need Justice, Lord, come by here
We need Justice, Lord, come by here
O Lord, come by here

They're killing our children Lord,
come by here . . .

Freedom Song [121S]

REMEMBER

When you have eaten your fill, and built fine houses and lived in them, and I have increased your herds and flocks, your silver and gold, and all your property, do not become haughty of heart and unmindful *of* the Lord, your God.

Otherwise, you might say to yourselves, "It is my own power and the strength of my own hand that has obt*ained* for me this wealth."

Remember then, it is the Lórd, your God who gives you the power *to* acquire wealth.

Deut. 8 in Gregorian Chant [1]

IT'S ME!

It's me, it's me, it's me, O Lord   D/G/Detc.
standin' in the need of prayer   (A)
It's me, it's me, it's me, O Lord
standin' in the need of prayer   (A)

Not my sister or my mother
but it's me, O Lord . . .

Not Republicans or Democrats
but me, O Lord . . .

Not the Russians or the Commies
but it's me, O Lord . . .

Not the rich man or the poor man
but it's me, O Lord . . .

Negro Spiritual [122]

O HEALING RIVER

O healing river   A/D
send down your waters!   A/D
Send down your waters   A
upon this land.   B/E

O healing river   A
send down your waters   C#/D
and wash the blood   B/A
from off the sand!   E/A

This land is parching
this land is thirsting.
No seed is growing
on this barren ground.
O healing river . . .

O seed of freedom
awake and flourish!
Let the deep roots nourish
let the tall stalk rise!
O healing river . . .

O seed of freedom
burst forth in glory
proud leaves unfurling
unto the skies.
O healing river . . .

Song by Fred Hellerman and Fran Minkof 123

I think that if the beast in man could be held down by threats — any kind of threat, whether of jail or retribution after death — then the highest emblem of humanity would be the lion tamer in the circus with the whip, not the prophet who sacrificed himself. But don't you see! This is just the point. What for centuries raised man above the beast is not the cudgel but an inward music, the irresistable power of unarmed truth, the powerful attraction of its example.
Boris Pasternak — Doctor Zhivago

Suffering

THE COST OF TRAVEL

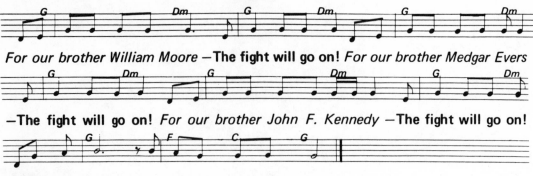

For our brother William Moore — **The fight will go on!** *For our brother Medgar Evers*

—The fight will go on! *For our brother John F. Kennedy* **—The fight will go on!**

Today we mourn —Tomorrow we move on!

For those four little girls
the fight will go on!
At the Sunday School they bombed
the fight will go on!
That was nineteen sixty-three
the fight will go on!
Today we mourn, tomorrow we move on

For our brother Michael Schwerner . . .
For our brother James Chaney . . .
For our brother Andrew Goodman . . .

For our brother Lemuel Penn . . .
For our brother Jim Reeb . . .
For our sister Viola Liuzzo . . .

For our brother Malcolm X . . .
For our brother Jonathan Daniels . . .
For our brother Samuel Younge . . .

For our brother Jimmy Jackson . . .
For our brother Martin King . . .
For our brother Robert Kennedy . . .

All you martyrs who have died . . .
Rest well in the earth . . .
Your work is done . . .

Our work has just begun . . .
You'll find new birth . . .
When we have won . . .

An abridged martyrology 1963-1968 [124]

WERE YOU THERE

Were you there when they	D/D7
crucified my Lord?	G/Em/D/G/D
Were you there when they	F#m
crucified my Lord?	G/Em-A

Sometimes it causes me	D/D7/G/Gm
to tremble, to tremble	D
Were you there when they	
crucified my Lord?	G/A/D/G/D

Were you there when they
bombed a house at night . . .

Were you there when they
turned away the poor . . .

Were you there when they
burned a land with bombs . . .

Adaptation of Negro Spiritual [125]

DEPORTEES

The crops are all in	D
and the peaches are rotting	G/D
The oranges are piled	
in their creosote dumps	G/D
You're flying them back	G
to Mexico border	D
to pay all their money	
to wade back again	G/D
Goodbye to my Juan	G
Goodbye Rosalita	D
Adios mi amigos	A7
Jesus and Maria	D
You won't have a name	G
When you ride the big airplane	D
And all they will call you	
Will be "deportee"	G/D

My father's own father
he waded that river
They took all the money
he made in his life

My brothers and sisters
come working the fruit trees
And they rode the truck
till they took down and died.
Goodbye to my Juan . . .

Some of us are illegal
and some are not wanted
Our work contract's out
and we have to move on
Six hundred miles
to that Mexican border
They chase us like outlaws
like rustlers, like thieves
Goodbye to my Juan . . .

We died in your hills
we died in your deserts
We died in your valleys
and died in your plains
We died 'neath your trees
and we died in your bushes
Both sides of the river
we died just the same
Goodbye to my Juan . . .

The sky plane caught fire
over Los Gatos Canyon
A fireball of lightning
and shook al' our hills
Who are all these friends
all scattered like dry leaves?
the radio says they are just deportees
Goodbye to my Juan . . .

Is this the best way
we can grow our big orchards?
Is this the best way
we can grow our good fruit?
To fall like dry leaves
to rot on my topsoil
and be called by no name
except "deportees"?
Goodbye to my Juan . . .

Words by Woodie Guthrie
Music by Martin Hoffman 126

OUT OF THE DEPTHS

Out of the depths
I cry to you O lord
Let your ears be attentive
to my pleading and entreating

Lord have mercy
Christ have mercy
Lord have mercy

Judge us not the cowardly way
we conform in judging our brothers
Forgive our idolatry of forms
and the evil in empty smiles
which hide all our ignorance
Lord have mercy . . .

Judge us not for making peace
with injustice and oppression
Forgive us for failing to help
the torn and battered lovers
who fight all our battles
Lord have mercy . ...

If you should keep a record
of our transgressions Lord
then who, Lord, could stand it?
But in your gift is pardon of sins
so that you may be served with dignity
Lord have mercy . . .

Chant based on Psalm 130 as sung by Clarence
Rivers 127

THE CONTINUING
STORY OF BUNGALOW BILL

When I came back [the Officer] had his
gun on Bug. He told the rest of the
group to get away or he would blow
Bug's brains out. So we moved back and
then all the rest of the police come.

So Bug was telling them that he was shot
. . . . So somebody says, "Nigger, where
you shot at?" And he says, "In my
back." . . . And they started pulling on
Bug.

His face, you know, he wasn't hollering
out in pain, but you could see the pain
in his face, you know, like his mouth
was open, like he couldn't close his
mouth or something. . . . I wondered
why they didn't take him to the hospital
right away, but they stayed around there
under the bridge for ten or twelve minutes.

[Later] we walked up to Number 14
Precinct and at that time I saw Mr.
Brooker. And I asked him what was up

and he said the police won't tell him
anything. He say. . .they say they shot
his son. . . .Then the ambulance come.

Testimony of Rufus "Catfish" Mayfield
at coroner's inquest

Hey, Bungalow Bill	C/G/C
What did you kill	Fm/C
Bungalow Bill?	Fm/C
Hey Bungalow Bill	A/E/A
What did you kill	Dm/A
Bungalow Bill?	Dm/E

He went out tiger hunting	Am/C
with his elephant and gun	F
In case of accidents	(G)/Am/C
he always took his mom	F
He's the all American	(G)/E/G
bullet-headed Saxon mother's son	Am/Fm

(All the children sing) Hey, Bungalow Bill

Deep in the jungle
where the mighty tiger lies
Bill and his elephants
were taken by surprise
So Captain Marvel zapped in
right between the eyes
(All the children sing) Hey, Bungalow Bill

The children asked him
if to kill was not a sin
But when he looked so fierce
his mother butted in
If looks could kill
it would have been us instead of him
(All the children sing) Hey, Bungalow Bill

Song by John Lennon and Paul McCartney [4]

SER COMO EL AIRE LIBRE

Ser como el aire libre	Am/Em
Just to be like the free wind!	
No más se pasa volando	B7/Em
Just passes through a flyin'	
Ser como la paloma	Am/Em
Just to be like a bird is	
También se pasa volando	B7/Em
Who passes too a flyin'	

Quando yo era chico
When I was a little boy
Mi madrecita decía
My dear mama used to tell me
Cuídate mi hijito
Watch out, little fellow
No te metas en líos
Don't go mixing into trouble
Ser como el aire libre. . .
Just to be like the free wind. . .

Y ahora que yo estoy grande
And now that I'm a big man
Estas palabras me duelen
These same words give me pain
Porque la vida es larga
Because I know that life is long
Y yo la paso llorando
And I pass through it a cryin'
Ser como el aire libre
Just to be like the free wind
No más se pasa volando
Just passes through a flyin'
Ser como el mar tan lindo
Just to be like the sea so lovely
También se pasa rodeando
All about us, all embracing

Song of the Delano Grape Strike, translated from the
Spanish by Richard J. Carr [128]

LONESOME VALLEY

If a man happens to be 36 years old, as I
happen to be, and some great truth
stands before the door of his life, some
great opportunity to stand up for that
which is right and that which is just, and
he refuses to stand up because he wants
to live a little longer and he is afraid his
home will get bombed, or he is afraid
that he will lose his job, or he is afraid
that he will get shot . . . he may go on and
live until he's 80, and the cessation of
breathing in his life is merely the belated
announcement of an earlier death of the
spirit.

Man dies when he refuses to stand up
for that which is right. A man dies when
he refuses to take a stand for that which
is true. So we are going to stand up right
here. . .letting the world know we are
determined to be free.

Martin Luther King, Jr.

Jesus walked that lonesome valley	F
He had to walk it by himself	C7/F
Oh, nobody else	C7/F
could walk it for him	Bb/F
He had to walk it by himself	Bb/F/C7/F

You got to walk your lonesome valley
you got to walk it by yourself
Oh, nobody else can walk it for you
you got to walk it by yourself

You must go and stand your trial
You have to stand it by yourself
Oh, nobody else can stand it for you
you have to stand it by yourself

White spiritual 129

Our firm intention to prevent further bloodshed does not mean passive acceptance of the situation that has risen. . . . We hope you will trust us even though we will have to take some temporary measures which will reduce the degree of democracy which we already have achieved. . . .

Dear listeners, please excuse that now and then there is a pause in my improvised speech. I believe you will understand why that is so. . . .

It will be harder and more difficult than imagined not too long ago. But, however life will continue, we must now think about ways of realizing in this new situation the program. . .we decided on in January. . . .

Alexander Dubcek, August 27, 1968

HARD TRAVELIN'

I've been doing some hard travelin'	G
I thought you knowed	
I've been doing some hard travelin'	
Way down the road	A7/D7
Well if you don't think	G
I've been through hell	G7
just follow me down	C
to the places I've been	
I've been doing	D7
some hard travelin', Lord	G

I've been walking
the streets of Washington. . .

I've been talking
to lots of Congressmen. . .

Make up your own verses.

Song by Woodie Guthrie 130

My God, My God, why have you forsaken me, far from my prayer, from *the* words I groan.

O, my God, I cry out by day, and you answer not; by night, and, there is *no* relief for me.

A pack of dogs surrounds me. A gang of villians closes in on me. They tie me hand and foot. I can count every one of my bones. They look on and gloat over me. They divide my garments among them and cast *lots* for my clothes.

Psalm 22 in Gregorian Chant [1]

THEY CAST THEIR NETS IN GALILEE

They cast their nets in Galilee	G/C
just off the hills of brown	G/Em
such happy, simple fisherfolk	G/Bm/Em
before the Lord came down	G/C

Contented, peaceful fishermen
before they ever knew
the peace of God that
filled their hearts
brimful—and broke them too

Young John who trimmed
the flapping sail
homeless, in Patmos died
Peter, who hauled
the teeming net
head-down was crucified

The peace of God, it is no peace
but strife closed in the sod
Yet, brothers, pray
for but one thing
the marvelous peace of God

Hymn by W.A. Percy to music by Herbert G. Draesel, Jr., "The Rejoice Mass" 131

Wherever death may surprise us, it will be welcome, provided that this, our battle cry, reach some receptive ear, that another stretch out to take up weapons; and that other men come forward to intone our funeral dirge with the staccato of machine guns and new cries of battle and victory.

Che

PRECIOUS DEATH

Precious in the sight of the Lord
is the death of his friends

How merciful the Lord, and just
How full of pity
He protects simple hearts
I was helpless, so he saved me

Turn back my soul to your rest
for the Lord had been good to you
He rescued you from death
and dried all your tears

Antiphon and chant based on Psalm 116 ¹³²

MICHAEL HAUL YOUR BOAT ASHORE

Michael haul your boat ashore	*D/G/D*
Alleluia	*G/F#m*
Then you'll hear the horn they blow	*G/Em*
Alleluia	*D/A7/D*

Then you'll hear the trumpet sound
Alleluia
Trumpet sound the world around
Alleluia

Trumpet sound the Jubilee
Alleluia
Trumpet sound for you and me
Alleluia

Trumpet sound for rich and poor
Alleluia
Michael haul your boat ashore
Alleluia

Negro Spiritual ¹³³ˢ

A MARTYR'S WELCOME

May the angels, dear Jack, lead you into paradise; may the martyrs receive you at your coming; may the spirit of God

embrace you; and may you—with all those who made the supreme sacrifice of dying for others—receive eternal rest and peace.

Cardinal Cushing at the funeral of John F. Kennedy

THOSE WHO SOW IN SORROW

Those who sow in sorrow	G
they will reap with joy	D
Those who sow in sorrow	
they will reap with joy	G
At night there may be tears	C
but dawn brings joy	
Weeping has been changed	A
to shouts of gladness	
Those who sow in sorrow. . .	D

Deliver us, O Lord
from bondage now
our withered hopes
and battered dreams renew
Those who sow in sorrow. . .

Alleluia! Alleluia! Alleluia!
Alleluia! Alleluia! Alleluia!
Those who sow in sorrow. . .

Song by Etienne Briere based on Psalm 126 ¹³⁴ˢ

WE'LL NEVER TURN BACK

We've been 'buked	D
and we've been scorned	G/D
We've been talked about	A7/D
sure as you're born	A7/Bm
But we'll never turn back	A7/D/A7/D
No, we'll never turn back	A7/D/A7/Bm
until we've all been freed	A7/D/G/D
and we have equality	A7/D/A7/D

We have served
our time in jail
with no money
for to go our bail
But we'll never turn back. . .

We have walked
in the shadows of death
We've had to walk
all by ourselves
But we'll never turn back. . .

Adaptation of Negro Spiritual by Bertha Gober 135

BAPTISM

When I received the news
that same bullet entered me
That bullet killed him
But by that bullet I was reborn
And I was reborn a Negro!

Yevgeny Yevtushenko

Creation MARRIAGE TO LIFE

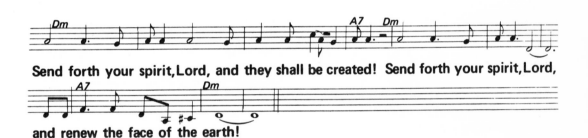

Send forth your spirit, Lord, and they shall be created! Send forth your spirit, Lord, and renew the face of the earth!

Peace on every mountain
justice on every hillside
He will defend the needy and friendless
and crush the oppressor

Like rain on the meadow
like raindrops descending to earth
In his day justice will flourish
and peace prevail

He will save the poor man
the afflicted, the helpless, the needy
He will have pity on the weak
and save the lives of the friendless

From fraud and violence
he will save them
Precious in his sight is their blood
Justice shall march before him
and peace shall follow his footsteps

Antiphon from Psalm 104
Verses from Psalms 72 and 85 in metrical chant 31

ABRAHAM AND SARAH

Abraham laughed and said to himself,
"Shall a son be born to one who is a
hundred years old? Shall Sarah who is
ninety bear a child?"

Sarah no longer had periods as is custom-
ary with women. So Sarah laughed to
herself and said, "Now that I am grown
old and my husband is old, shall *I* have
pleasure?"

The Lord said to Abraham, "Why did
Sarah laugh, is anything too *wonderful*
for the Lord?"

Sarah conceived and bore Abraham a
son in his old age and Abraham called
the son Isaac.

Sarah said, "God has given me cause for
laughter, and whoever hears of *it* will
laugh with me."

Genesis 17, 18, 21 in Gregorian Chant 1

SHOUT FOR JOY!

O Lord, shout for joy!
O Lord, shout for joy!
Early in the mornin' — shout for joy!
Late in the evenin' — shout for joy!

O Lord, shout for joy!
O Lord, shout for joy!
Feel like laughin' — shout for joy!
Feel like shoutin' — shout for joy!

O Lord, shout for joy!
O Lord, shout for joy!
Feel like singin' — shout for joy!
Feel like prayin' — shout for joy!

O Lord, shout for joy!
O Lord, shout for joy!
Now I'm gettin' happy — shout for joy!
Feel like dancin' — shout for joy!

Negro Spiritual 137

VIRGIN MARY

The Virgin Mary had a baby boy!	E/B7
The Virgin Mary had a baby boy!	E
The Virgin Mary had a baby boy!	A
And they say	E
that his name was Jesus	B7/E

He come from the glory	E/B
He come from the glorious kingdom	E/B/E
He come from the glory	B7
He come from	E
the glorious kingdom	B7/E/A
O yes, Believer!	E/A
O yes, Believer!	E
He come from the glory	B7/E
He come from the glorious kingdom	B7/E

The wise men came
when the baby was born. . .

The angels sang
when the baby was born. . .

West Indies Song 138

HAVA NAGILA

Hava nagila, hava nagila	D
hava nagila venismecha!	D#/D
Hava nagila, hava nagila	
hava nagila venismecha!	D#/D
Hava neranena, have neranena	Cm
nava neranena venismecha!	D
Have neranena, hava neranena	Cm
have neranena venismecha!	D
Uru, Uru, Uru achim b'lev samayach!	Gm
Uru achim b'lev samayach	Cm
Uru achim b'lev samayach	
Uru achim, Uru achim	D
b'lev samayach	Gm/D/Gm

Jewish Song. It says be happy. 139

CREATION

True as God's Word! I have life in my
body! This dead tree, my body has
burst in flower! You've given me life! . . .
Unpack the box! Unpack the box with
the Christmas ornaments in it, put them
on me, brass bells and glass birds and
stars and tinsel and snow! I've won, I've
won, Mr. Death, I'm going to bear!

Tennessee Williams, Orpheus Descending

TWELVE DAYS OF CHRISTMAS

On the first day of Christmas
my true love gave to me
a partridge in a pear tree

On the second day of Christmas
my true love gave to me
two turtle doves
and a partridge in a pear tree

On the third day of Christmas
my true love gave to me
three French hens
two turtle doves
and a partridge in a pear tree

. . .four mocking birds

. . .five golden rings

. . .six geese a laying

. . .seven swans a swimming

. . .eight maids a milking

. . .nine ladies waiting

. . .ten lords a leaping

. . .leven pipers piping

. . .twelve drummers drumming

Old English Song 140

The book talks about man being made in the image and likeness of God. . .and we get the idea that man is called to be like God

> as creator
> as maker

In a sense every man is supposed to be an artist.

> That's the word.

Corita Kent

GO TELL IT ON THE MOUNTAIN

Go tell it on the mountain	E
Over the hills and everywhere	B7/E
Go tell it on the mountain	
That Jesus Christ is here	B7/E

Once we were so proud and strong	
We lived all to ourselves	A7/E
We see our God in brothers now	
in this strength is our help	F#7/B7
Go tell it on the mountain. . .	

When I was a seeker
I sought both night and day
I asked the Lord to help me
and he showed me the way
Go tell it on the mountain. . .

He made me a watchman
upon the city wall
and if I am a Christian
I am the least of all
Go tell it on the mountain. . .

Adaptation of Negro Spiritual 141S

MAN

When I see the heavens
the work of your hands
the moon and the stars
which you arranged

what is man
that you keep him in mind
mortal man
that you should care for him?

Yet you have made him
little less than the angels
with glory and honor
you crowned him
gave him rule
over the works of your hand
put all things under his feet

All animals, sheep and cattle
yes, even the savage beasts
birds of the air, and fish of the sea
you have made subject to man

I thank you that I am so wonderfully made and for the wonders of all creation.

Psalms 8 and 139 in metrical chant 31

THIS LITTLE LIGHT

The artist is the sign to the whole world that the world is shaped by man and not the other way around.

Corita Kent

This little light of mine	G
I'm gonna let it shine	G7
This little light of mine	C
I'm gonna let it shine	G
This little light of mine	
I'm gonna let it shine	B7/Em
Let it shine, let it shine	G/D7
let it shine	Em

All around the town. . .

Free of fear and hatred . . .

The light that shines	G
is the light of love	
lights the darkness	C
from above	
It shines on me	G
and it shines on you	
shows what the power	A7
of love can do	D7
I'm gonna shine my light	G
both far and near	
I'm gonna shine my light	C

both bright and clear   *C7*
Where there's a dark corner   *G*
in this land   *B7/Em*
I'm gonna let   *A7*
my little light shine!   *D7/G*

Building up a new world . . .

Some say "It's dark
we cannot see"
but love lights up
the world for me
Some say "Turn around
and just go and hide"
but love has the power
to brave the tide
Some see it as
a sad old story
but we see a world
that's bound for glory
The spirit says
we have the power divine
so let your little light shine!

Adaptation of Freedom Song 142

VAL: You lived in Two River County, the wife of the County sheriff. You saw awful things take place. Beatings! Lynchings! Runaway convicts torn to pieces by hounds! . . .But violence is not quick always. Sometimes it's slow. Some tornadoes are slow. Corruption rots men's hearts and rot is slow. . . .
VEE: How do you know?
VAL: I been a witness, I know!
VEE: I been a witness, I know!
VAL: We seen these things from seats down front at the show. And so you begun to paint your visions. Without no plan, no training, you started . . . as if God touched your fingers. You made some beauty out of this dark country with these two, soft, woman's hands. . . .

Tennessee Williams, Orpheus Descending

JOY TO THE WORLD

Joy to the world! The Lord is come!
Let earth receive her king!
Let every heart prepare him room!

and heaven and nature sing
and heaven and nature sing
and heaven, and heaven
and nature sing!

Joy to the world! The Savior reigns!
Let men their songs employ!
While fields and flood
rocks, hills and plains
repeat the sounding joy
repeat the sounding joy
repeat, repeat the sounding joy!

Isaac Watts to the music of Lowell Mason (1833)

Like it or not we live in times of danger and uncertainty. But they are also more open to the creative energy of men than any other time in history.

Robert F. Kennedy

RISE UP SHEPHERD

There's a star in the east   *A*
on Christmas morn
Rise up shepherd and follow   *E/A*
It'll lead to the place
where the Savior's born
Rise up shepherd and follow   *|E/A*

Leave your sheep
and leave your lambs   *D*
Rise up shepherd and follow   *G/A*
Leave your ewes
and leave your rams   *D*
Rise up shepherd and follow   *E/A*

Follow, follow   *E/D/A*
Rise up shepherd and follow   *G/A*
Follow the star of Bethlehem   *D/A*
Rise up shepherd and follow   *E/A*

If you follow a star that's bright. . .
You must travel free and light. . .

If you're gonna follow your star. . .
You must begin right where you are. . .

Adaptation of Negro Spiritual 143S

I WANT TO BE READY

I want to be ready!	E
I want to be ready!	A/E/C#m
I want to be ready!	A/E
Workin' for freedom	C#m
just like John!	A/E

John, O John, what did he say?	A/E
Workin' for freedom	C#m
just like John!	A/E
"Clear the way people	
for the final day"	A/E
Workin' for freedom	C#m
just like John!	A/E
I want to be ready. . .	

John, O John, he helped clear the way
Workin' for freedom, just like John!
Said the work won't be finished
in a hundred days!
Workin' for freedom, just like John!
I want to be ready. . .

John, O John, when will we win?
Workin' for freedom, just like John!
"That's hard to answer
but we must begin" . . .

John ,O John, took Peter's oars
Workin' for freedom, just like John!
Said "The Church needs a lot more
open doors " . . .

John , O John, what did they do?
Workin' for freedom, just like John!
"They started into buildin' up
somethin' new " . . .

Adaptation of Negro Spiritual [144s]

There are some souls particularly endowed with generosity, who, on finding situations where the requirements of justice are not being satisfied or not satisfied in full, feel enkindled with the desire to change the state of things, as if they wished to have recourse to something like a revolution.

. . .to establish with truth, justice, charity, and liberty new methods of relationships in human society: the relations among individual citizens, among citizens and their own country, among nations themselves, among individuals, families, intermediate associations and individual states on the one hand, and with the community of all mankind on the other. . . .

Every believer in this world of ours must be a spark of light, a center of love, a vivifying leaven amidst his fellowmen.

Pope John XXIII, Pacem In Terris

GO WHERE I SEND THEE

Children go where I send thee!	C
How shall I send thee?	F/C

I shall send thee one by one	
Cause one was the little bitty baby	
wrapped in swaddling clothing	
lying in a manger	
Born, born, born	C/F/C
in Bethlehem!	G/C

I shall send thee two by two
Cause two was Paul and Silas
One was the little bitty baby. . .

. . .Three was the Hebrew children

. . .Four was the four
come knockin' at the door

. . .Five was the Gospel preachers

. . .Six was the six
that couldn't get fixed

. . .Seven was the seven
went up to heaven

. . .Eight was the eight
stood at the gate

. . .Nine was the nine
got left behind

. . .Ten was the ten Commandments

An Old Fun Song [145]

NOTHING IS PROFANE TO THOSE WHO KNOW HOW TO SEE
Teilhard de Chardin

DE COLORES

De colores, de colores se visten   G
All in color, all in color the fields
los campos en la primavera   D7
love to dress in all during the springtime
De colores, de colores son los   C
All in color, all in color the birds
pajarillos que vienen de afuera   G
have their clothing that comes every season
De colores, de colores es el   G7
All in color, all in color the rainbow
arcoiris que vemos lucir   C
is vested across the blue sky
Y por eso los grandes amores de   G
And so you see that so must all love be
muchos colores me gustan a mi   D/G
of every bright color to make my heart sing
Y por eso los grandes amores de   C/G
And so you see that so must all love be
muchos colores me gustan a mi   D/G
of every bright color to make my heart sing

Canta el gallo, canta el gallo
Sings the rooster, sings the rooster
con el quire, quire, quire
with his quire, quire, quire
quire quire quire quire
quire quire quire quire
La gallina, la gallina con la
and the cluck-hen, and the cluck hen with her
cara cara cara cara cara cara cara
cara cara cara cara cara cara cara
El polluelo, el polluelo con el
and the babe-chicks, and the babe chicks with their
peo peo peo peo peo peo pa
peo peo peo peo peo peo pa
Se hace un león con su quire quire
becomes like a lion with their quire quire
cara cara peo peo pa
cara cara, peo peo pa
Y por eso los grandes amores de
And so you see that so must all love be
muchos colores me gustan a mi.
of every bright color to make my heart sing

Song of the Cursillistas 146s

Evil may be not seeing well enough; so perhaps to become less evil we need only to see more. . . .Hence everybody is in the game. Things look different to different people depending on where they stand. If we share views — not convert others to our views — we would get a larger vision.

Corita Kent

⚘ WE'RE GONNA MOVE

We're gonna move   C
when the spirit says move!
We're gonna move
when the spirit says move!   C7
Cause when the spirit says move   F
then you move with the spirit   G7/C
Gotta move
when the spirit says move!   G7/C

We're gonna sing. . .

We're gonna march. . .

We're gonna talk. . .

Freedom Song 147

FILLED WITH LIFE

Oh hallelujah!   Dm/C/A
My soul glorifies the Lord!   C/Dm/A
O hallelujah!   Dm/C/A
My heart leaps for joy!   F/Em/A
Oh hallelujah!   Dm
God has done   E/Am
great things for me!   Em/E/Am
Oh hallelujah!   Dm/C/A
I'm filled with life!   Em/Dm

To me his servant
humble and lowly   A/Dm
he comes and brings with him
a great new life   F/Em/A
Thus he shows in every generation   Dm/Am/C
love and kindness   Dm
towards all his friends   A/Dm
Oh hallelujah. . . .

He shows his arm in strength
cutting down the mighty
kings toppled from their thrones
the low raised high
His best gifts
he showers on the hungry man
rich men he sends away
alone with empty hands
Oh hallelujah. . . .

Magnificat (Luke 1) set to early American hymn tune 148S

SOME MEN SEE THINGS AS THEY ARE AND SAY, "WHY?" I DREAM THINGS THAT NEVER WERE AND SAY, "WHY NOT?"
Robert F. Kennedy

The Kingdom *A FREE COMMUNITY*

THE FOOL

I have squandered the splendid years
that the Lord gave to my youth
In attempting impossible things
deeming them alone worth the toil

The lawyers have sat in council
the men with the keen long faces
and said, "This man is a fool"
and others have said, "He blasphemeth"

O wise men riddle me this:
What if the dream come true?

Padriac Pearce in metrical chant 31

BEAUTIFUL CITY

O what a beautiful city!	C
O what a beautiful city!	G
O what a beautiful city!	C
Twelve gates to the city!	F9
Hal le loo yah!	C/F/C/G7
In the new Jerusalem	C
I'll sing and shout	F
There's twelve gates to the city!	C/F/C
Ain't no race of men	
gonna be kept out!	F
There's twelve gates to the city!	C/F/C
Hal le loo yah!	F/C/F/C/G7
O what a beautiful city . . .	

See the city all sparklin' and new!
There's twelve gates to the city!
For the twelve tribes of Israel
apostles too
There's twelve gates to the city!
Hal le loo yah!
O what a beautiful city. . .

Everybody's welcome there
rich and poor!
There's twelve gates to the city!
Death and sorrow will be no more
There's twelve gates to the city!
Hal le loo yah!
O what a beautiful city. . .

See the home of God is among all men
There's twelve gates to the city!

They'll all live in peace
as he walks with them. . . .

The city's gates will be open doors!
There's twelve gates to the city!
The things that cursed mankind
will be no more!. . .

Adaptation of Negro Spiritual 149S

THE PROUD TRAMPLED UNDER—FOOT BY THE NEEDY

The Lord enters into judgment with his people's elders and princes: It is you who have devoured the vineyard; the loot wrested from the poor is in your houses. What do you mean by crushing my people, and grinding down the poor *when* they look to you?

Woe to those who enact unjust statutes and who write oppressive decrees, depriving the needy of judgment and robbing my people's poor of their rights, making widows their *plunder* and orphans their prey

He humbles those in high places, and the lofty city he brings down. He tumbles it to the ground, *levels* it with the dust.

It is trampled underfoot by the needy, by the *footsteps* of the poor.

Isaiah 3, 10, 26 in Gregorian Chant 1

THIS LAND IS YOUR LAND

This land is your land. . .	G/C
this land is my land	G
from California	D7
to the New York Island	G
From the Redwood Forest	C
to the Gulf Stream Waters	G
This land was made for you and me	D7/G

As I was walking that ribbon of highway
I saw above me the endless skyway
I saw below me that golden valley
This land was made for you and me

I've roamed and rambled
and I've followed my footsteps
to the sparkling sand of
her diamond deserts
and all around me
a voice was calling
This land belongs to you and me
This land is your land. . .

When the sun came shining
and I was strolling
And the wheat fields waving
and the dustclouds rolling
As the fog was lifting
a voice was calling
This land was made for you and me
This land is your land. . .

Song by Woodie Guthrie 150

THE GREAT HALLELU

Hallay! Hallelujah!   *A7/Dm/A7/Dm*
Hallay! Hallelu!   *A7/Dm/A7/Dm*
Hallay! Hallelujah!   *A7/Dm/A7/Dm*
Hallay! Hallelu!   *A7/Dm/A7/Dm*
Repeat 4 times, faster each time

He raises the poor from the dust   *Dm/A7*
from the garbage heap   *Dm*
he lifts up the lowly   *A7/Dm*
Sing out the great hallelu!   *A7/Dm*
Hallay! Hallelujah. . .

He seats them with the rich
and with rulers of nations
Sing out the great hallelu!
Hallay! Hallelujah!

He gives the childless women
a joyful home
with children to mother
Sing out the great hallelu!
Hallay! Hallelujah. . .

Antiphon by Paul Quinlan. Verses from Psalm 113
translated by Allene Guss Grognet and set to metrical
chant 151

THE MILL WAS MADE OF MARBLE

I dreamed that I had died   *C/G7/C*
And gone to my reward   *F/C*
A job in heaven's textile plant   *F/C*
On a golden boulevard   *G/G7/C*

The Mill was made of marble   *C/G7/C*
The machines   *C7/F*
were made out of gold   *c*
And nobody ever got tired *C7/F/Cdim/C/Am*
And nobody ever grew old   *Dm7/G7/C*

It was oh, so peaceful in heaven
There was no clatter or boom
You could hear the most
beautiful music
As you worked
at the spindle and loom

There was no unemployment in heaven
We worked steady all through the year
We always had food for the children
We never were haunted by fear

When I woke from this dream
about heaven
I wondered if someday there'd be
A mill like that one down below
here on earth
For workers like you and like me

Soñé que había muerto
Y hacia el cielo me fuí
Me dieron trabajo ahí en el taller
De su gran fabrica textil

Las máchinas eran de oro
De mármol era el taller
Allí nadie se cansó nunca
Ni nadie llegó a envejecer

Allá en el cielo lindo
Sin ruido para molestar
Se oye música angelical
Allí junto a mi telar

La palabra desempleo
Jamás se usaba allá
El sueldo siempre alcanza a pagar
El gasto de cada hogar

Mi sueño fué dorado
Yo sé que no era verdad
Tal vez un día se convertirá
En una feliz realidad

Song by Joe Glazer. Versión en Español por Genaro
Villarreal y Sra. Esther Galli 152

A CHILD'S DREAM

Q. Why was Martin Luther King famous?
A. Martin Luther King was famous because he did everything he wasn't supposed to do.

Q. Can a white person be a soul brother?
A. Yes. He can't help it if he was born white.

Q. What was Martin Luther King's dream?
A. He dreamed that up in heaven all the black children and white children would be playing ring around the rosies together.

I had a dream this very night	D
about the war for civil rights	A/D
I dreamed that	
we had stopped the war	
and lived in peace forever more	A/D

I dreamed of Martin Luther King	G/D
and all the love he tried to bring	A/D
I saw him in the promised land	G/D
where black and white	A
walk hand in hand	D

I can't forget the night he died
It was so sad I cried and cried
For civil rights he'll march no more
He's resting on that golden shore
I dreamed of Martin Luther King. . .

Though Martin Luther King is gone
I know his dream still marches on
He saw the best in every man
We must complete what he began
I dreamed of Martin Luther King. . .

Freedom for all that was his goal
He tried to touch each person's soul
You might be black or white or blue
To him you were soul brothers too
I dreamed of Martin Luther King. . .

Song by Joe Glazer. He writes: "This song was inspired by and based on the booklet 'Children of Cardozo Tell It Like It Is,' compiled from the questions, writings and drawings of District of Columbia public school children, grades 1-8, reacting to the assassination of Martin Luther King." 153s

BLACKBIRD

Blackbird singing	G/Am7
in the dead of night	G
take these broken wings	C/A7/D
and learn to fly	Adim/Em-Eb
All your life	D/C-Cm
you were only waiting	G/A7
for this moment to arise	D7/G

Blackbird singing
in the dead of night
taken these sunken eyes
and learn to see
All your life
you were only waiting
for this moment to be free

Blackbird fly!	F/C/Bb-C
Blackbird fly!	F/C/Bb-A7
Into the light	Bb
of the dark black night!	G
Blackbird fly!	
Blackbird fly!	
into the light	
of the dark black night!	

Blackbird singing
in the dead of night [
take these broken wings
and learn to fly
All your life
you were only waiting
for this moment to arise
You were only waiting
for this moment to arise
You were only waiting
for this moment to arise

Song by John Lennon and Paul McCartney [4]

THE GATHERED BREAD

As this piece of bread was scattered over the mountain and then was gathered together and made one, so let your people be gathered from the ends of the earth into your kingdom, O Lord!

Early Christian Eucharistic prayer from the Didache

THE WELCOME TABLE

We're gonna sit	G
at the welcome table!	G7
We're gonna sit	C
at the welcome table	
one of these days! Hallelujah!	G7/D7
We're gonna sit	G
at the welcome table!	B7/Em
Gonna sit at the welcome table	C/D7
one of these days!	G

All kinds of people
around that table. . .

Won't be no fightin'
around that table. . .

Sinners and outcasts
around that table. . .

No fancy style
at the welcome table. . .

Won't be no grabbin'
around that table. . .

Start to gather now
at the welcome table. . .

Open up the doors
to the welcome table. . .

Tear down the walls
built around that table. . .

Adaptation of Negro Spiritual 154S

SHALOM ALECHEM

Black and White is not color no more,
it's an attitude. . . Every day more
people wake up black than went to bed
black.

Dick Gregory

Havenu Shalom Alechem!	Cm/G7/Cm/G7/Cm
Havenu Shalom Alechem!	C7/Fm
Havenu Shalom Alechem!	G7/Cm/G7/Cm
Havenu Shalom! Shalom!	G7
Shalom Alechem!	Cm

*An old Hebrew song. It means a lot more than "Peace
be to you." It's something more like sharing oneself
with another. 155S*

A KINGDOM OF UNITED NATIONS

He shall raise a signal to the nations and
gather the outcasts of Israel. The dis-
persed of Juda he shall assemble from
the four corners of the earth.

The envy of Ephraim shall pass away,
and the rivalry of Juda be removed.
Ephraim shall not be jealous of Juda,
and Juda shall not be hostile to Ephraim.

Isaiah 11

No more shall the sound
of the war whoop be heard
the ambush and slaughter
no longer be feared
The tomahawk buried
shall rest in the ground
and peace and goodwill
to the nations abound
The tomahawk buried
shall rest in the ground
and peace and goodwill
to the nations abound

All spirit of war
to the gospel shall bow
The bow lie unstrung
at the foot of the plow
To prune the young orchard
the spear shall be bent
And love greet the world
with a smile of content
To prune the young orchard
the spear shall be bent
And love greet the world
with a smile of content

White Spiritual 156

GOD IS HERE

God is here, my brother	C
God is here	F/C
God is here, my brother	Em
God is here	F/G7
God is here my brother	C
God is here	F/C
O Lord, God is here	F/C/G7/C

Someone's crying, Lord
God is here . . .

Someone's laughing, Lord
God is here . . .

Someone's working, Lord . . .

Someone's playing, Lord . . .

God is black, my brother . . .

God is white, my brother . . .

Adaptation of Negro Spiritual, "Come By Here" [121s]

HINEY MATOV

Hiney matov u'mana'im	Gm/Dm

How good and pleasant the time is here

shevet achim gam yachad!	C/Dm

all men can live together!

Hiney matov u'mana'im	Gm/Dm

How good and pleasant the time is here

shevet achim gam yachad	C/Dm

all men can live together!

Hiney matov! Hiney Matov!	G/Dm/G

How good and pleasant! How good and pleasant!

Lalalalalalalalalala	C/Dm

Lalalalalalalalalala

Hiney matov! Hiney matov!	G/Dm/G

How good and pleasant! How good and pleasant!

Lalalalalalalalalala	C/Dm

Lalalalalalalalalala

Hiney matov u'mana'im	Gm/Dm

How good and pleasant the time is here

shevet achim gam yachad!	C/Dm

all men can live together!

Hiney matov u'mana'im	Gm/Dm

How good and pleasant the time is here

shevet achim gam yachad!	C/Dm

all men can live together!

Hiney matov u'mana'im	F/C

How good and pleasant the time is here

Hiney matov u'mana'im	F/C

How good and pleasant the time is here

Hiney matov u'mana'im	Dm/Am

How good and pleasant the time is here

Hiney matov u'mana'im	Dm/G/Dm

How good and pleasant the time is here

Hebrew song based on Psalm 133
translated by Allene Guss Grognet [157s]

I'VE GOT THAT JOY

I've got that joy, joy, joy, joy	C
down in my heart down in my heart	G7
down in my heart!	C

I've got that joy, joy, joy, joy	
down in my heart	
down in my heart to stay!	G7/C

I've got that joy of living . . .

I've got that love of freedom . . .

I've got that love of all
my brothers and my sisters . . .

I've got that peace that surpasses
all understanding . . .

Adaptation of old revival hymn [158s]

AMERICA THE BEAUTIFUL

My father — who was a small businessman — came here in 1893, on a business
trip, and fell in love with the country,
and particularly with the spirit of freedom that was in the air. And so he
persuaded my mother to uproot the
family, and from the moment we landed
on Manhattan I knew, with the sure
instinct of a child, that this was my
native spiritual home.

Felix Frankfurter

O beautiful for spacious skies
For amber waves of grain
For purple mountains majesties
Above the fruited plain
America, America
God shed his grace on thee
And crown your good with brotherhood
From sea to shining sea

O beautiful for heroes proved
In liberating strife
Who more than self their country loved
And mercy more than life
America, America
May God your good refine
'Till all success be nobleness
And every gain divine

Song by Katherine Lee Bates and Samuel A. Ward

HALLELUJAH! HALLELUJAH!
HALLELUJAH! HALLELUJAH!
HALLELUJAH!
HALLELUJAH! HALLELUJAH!
HALLELUJAH! HALLELUJAH!
HALLELUJAH

From the Hallelujah Chorus of J. F. Handel

Everybody sing   FREEDOM!
                 FREEDOM!
                 FREEDOM!
                 FREEDOM!
                 FREEDOM!
All the world around
                 FREEDOM! . . .

Freedom Song("Amen" from Lilies of the Fields) 159s

O Lord, who delivered us and delivered our fathers, and brought us to this night of sharing and eating together, bring us to other meals and to other festive gatherings.   Make us happy in the building of your city, and joyous in your service.   And may we always sing songs of thanks to you, our God, who continually fills our living with life.

Adaptation of blessing at conclusion of Passover Meal

Shalom Havayreem Shalom Havayreem
Shalom Shalom Shalom Havayreem
Shalom Havayreem Shalom Shalom

Hebrew song, "Peace my friends," a kind of group Shalom or sharing 160S

O when the saints go marchin' in!
O when the saints go marchin' in!
I want to be in that number
When the saints go marchin' in!

O when the new world is complete. . .

When brother   goes marchin' in. . .

When sister   goes marchin' in. . .

O when they blow that golden horn. . .

O when they're singin' hellelu. . .

O when the Lord is shakin' hands. . .

Negro Spiritual 161

We are moving into a bright day of Freedom. We, through our struggles, through our suffering, through our sacrifices, will be able to achieve the American dream. This will be the day when all of God's children — black men and white men; Jews and Gentiles; Protestants and Catholics — will be able to join hands and sing, in the words of the old Negro spiritual, "Free at last! Free at last! Thank God Almighty! We are Free at last!

Martin Luther King, Jr.

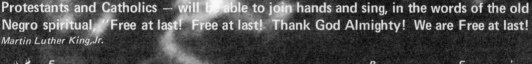

Free at last! Free at last! Thank God A'mighty I'm free at last! Free at last!

Free at last! Thank God A'mighty I'm free at last! *One of these mornings*

bright and fair—Thank God A'mighty I'm free at last! *I'm gonna put on my wings*

and try the air —Thank God A'mighty I'm free at last!

Ol' Satan's mad because we're glad! Thank God A'mighty we're free at last! *He missed a crowd he thought he had!* Thank God A'mighty we're free at last! Free at last . . .

I wonder what ol' Satan's grumblin' bout! Thank God A'mighty we're free at last!
Cause he's chained in Hell and he can't get out! Thank God A'mighty we're free at last!

Negro Spiritual as sung by Mother Scott 162

Sing to the Lord a NEW SONG

This collection of notes is concerned with technique and references. It is separate from the poetry in the front of the book because technique and scholarship are not supposed to show. Here you will find

A. An introductory discussion of the Technique of Celebration and Singing.

B. A brief explanation of the chord symbols used in the text

C. A discussion and list of general musical references together with the initial letters by which they are designated in the notes which follow.

D. Specific Notes, numbered to correspond to those at the end of credit lines in the front of the book, which may include references to music, books, records, history, singing technique, and last but not least, a copyright notice. All material noted herein is used by permission of the copyright owners. All rights reserved. We are extremely grateful to the many music and book publishers who, through their generosity in granting permissions, made this book possible. We trust you will respect this generosity by not reproducing any of the material herein without their express permission.

E. Spirituals for City People. Some of the numbers have an "s" after them. This indicates musical notation is included in this special collection and set out on pages following the text of these notes under the same corresponding number. A general discussion of this collection is included at the end of the specific notes headed, SPIRITUALS FOR CITY PEOPLE.

F. A select bibliography of non-musical publications quoted or referred to in the text, together with the copyright notice. All such material noted herein is used by permission of the copyright owners. All rights reserved. We are grateful and trust you will be respectful.

A. TECHNIQUE OF CELEBRATION

Learning has gotten very dull, but that is because schools have confined it to unimportant things. JTF grew out of different soil. It is the outgrowth of the experience of a number of people in planning and executing what we have come to call a " celebration." This can be a party at home, a gathering in a park, a service in church, or a demonstration out on the streets. It can be as small as a group in your living room or as large as a giant political rally.

The last of these we like to remember was the visit of the late Robert Kennedy to the people he loved, and who loved him so much, in the heart of Washington's Black Community last spring. A group of African drummers summoned the crowd which grew eventually to about 15,00 people. There was song, and talk, and—even in a crowd that large—dialogue. People were talking and singing back. Participation had set in. Nearly everyone there was involved in a very personal way in something important.

No technique or gimmick—musical or otherwise—caused this to happen. A celebration cannot be artifically inseminated. It has to be real. What technique did was to facilitate its happening and not interfere with it once it got started.

Corita Kent explains it this way: A man "creates many small ceremonies and celebrations all day long—if he has any health. He laughs and cries and shouts in expressing the delight and sorrow and anger which arise in him—or descend into him. These ceremonies underline the importance of each emotion and emotions are what keeps the human race running. . . . Maybe the same thing happens to the whole human running race. When it can no longer express its own human feelings—of love and anger, of joy and hope and despair—it becomes deformed. . . . And then it strikes out destructively.

"When groups of humans get bigger—too big for a hug, too many for a single groan—then ceremony gets more complex and someone needs to direct the traffic. . . . Someone's got to order the groceries. But if he only knows physical facts and knows no poetry or irony . . . the people will go hungry and will be unable to express and explain themselves to each other. They will disintegrate. [A good planning group] talks about how to arrange a day so that people can act humanly without embarrassment. It talks about building a gentle structure that supports just enough so that the thing can go up. A good structure makes freer than no structure because it supports. But very soon when the thing is built the structure is dissolved." (Footnotes and Headlines, Herder & Herder, 1967)

Sadly enough the grocery ordering has been so inept, and the structures imposed so rigid that people seldom have the opportunity to celebrate these days. This lack of authentic ritual in our culture is a sign of considerable danger if we are to take seriously the writings of psychiatrists like Erich Fromm. The authoritarianism in our rituals can readily be seen in the architecture of public gathering places—auditoriums, churches, theatres—where it is strictly eyes front and follow the leader. The kind of liberating structures we would like to see are best illustrated by John Hart in his description of The Action Mass (CBS Dimension, August 22, 1967):

"Dear Harry: We finally found the oldest, established, permanent, floating church service in Washington. . . .

"The first thing you notice about this floating parish, Harry, is that it has no place to sit. The portable parishioners prefer to have no place to sit, unless it is on the floor. They feel that furniture is inhibiting, expecially church pews. As one of them said, 'Pews keep people in line, everybody facing front. They put all that wood between you and your neighbor. Nobody behaves that way any other place than church.'

"The Action Mass is celebrated in a different place each Sunday. We found it in a gymnasium on the edge of a Washington slum. Organ music was replaced by the strum of folk guitars and bongo drums. They move around, says one, 'to get out of the geographical bag the cities are in.' The idea is to draw in the people whose frames and minds would not be comfortable in a traditional church, sitting in pews with people who are used to orderliness and calm; to draw in people who are on the disorderly edge of society.

"The striking part of all this was the behavior of the children. There were a lot of them there. Everywhere there. Some perched on the shoulders of their fathers to see better, some sitting listening, others playing on the unused stage in the gymnasium. Nobody turned around to stare when they fidgeted, and when some of them laughed out loud no one shushed them. Most of them sat in bunches with their friends and most of the time decided to pay attention. The kids actually seemed to enjoy church. And the adults seemed to like that.

"The grownups seemed especially to like the part right after the sermon called the dialogue-homily, when they could tell the priest what they thought, too, One of the young men with a guitar said he came to church prepared to be angry at hearing platitudes. But he hadn't heard any yet, so he liked it.

"At one point the priest walked to the person nearest him and shook his hand saying, 'Peace be with you.' That person did the same to someone near, and pretty soon the handshake had spread through all the people there.

"One Sunday, the Action Mass went to the heart of hippieland in Washington: DuPont Circle where, as you know Harry, the hippies hang out. Some signs showed up at that service. Signs, like 'Set Free' and 'Come alive' and 'Hurray!' On the edge of the crowd one hippie asked another if he went for this religious stuff. The other beard replied, 'I don't know, but the music and the signs are good.' The next day, the hippie newspaper, the Free Press gave it big coverage.

"Last Sunday, the service ended with everyone singing Shalom—a reminder that their church was founded by a Jew.

"As we left, we overheard a visitor say he felt that Jew in a homespun seamless robe would probably be at home there.

"And his friend said, 'Maybe he was.' "

A NEW SONG

Because our recent social experience has been so authoritarian, and therefore isolating, we looked deep into our past for some new ideas. We looked to the techniques of the ancient folk chants: Hebrew psalms, Christian plainchant, and the continuing African tradition. We looked also to the American expression of these traditions in the music of the poor churches of America, the Negro and White Spirituals and their direct carry-overs to the Labor Movement picket line and the more recent Civil Rights demonstrations. These techniques are discussed in the notes which follow, especially those numbered 1,3,7s,29s,30,31,42,61,&79.

It is interesting to compare these traditions. Listen to the isolated Negro communities of the Georgia Sea Islands ("Southern Journey" by Alan Lomax, Prestige International). Their singing,especially when accompanied by drums, reminds us of the way in which Jewish communities, isolated for centuries, sing the psalms. Israeli scientists believe that groups like the Yemenites, the Jews of Cochin, the Caucuses, and others sing the biblical chants today much as their ancestors did two or three thousand years ago in Israel. Listen to "Music in Israel Today" (Westminster Collectors Album) and two popular singers and musicologists, Hillel and Aviva—"Land of Milk and Honey" (Riverside). Medieval European chant, performed according to the best available historical information, as in the "Play of Daniel" (New York Pro Musica under direction of the late Noah Greenberg, Decca) discloses the same basic feeling and movement; the same insistent rhythm; the same extensive use of percussion instruments; and the same expressive, frequently sensual, singing style. So it would seem that we are all cousins: the Jews at the time of Jesus, the Catholics of Medieval Europe, and the Negro Baptists of America.

One thing we would emphasize about these traditions is their creative impulse. Within their "gentle structure" there is always an invitation to spontaneous improvisation. In *Nobody Knows My Name*, James Baldwin, writing about the African attitude toward art, puts it this way: "Art itself is taken to be perishable, to be made again each time it disappears or is destroyed. What is clung to is the spirit which makes art possible." The dynamic is not to be imprisoned, idol-like, in some work of the past. Nothing could be more opposed to the African creative principle than an attempt to sing psalms or spirituals as they were sung years ago, or last year, or even ten minutes ago. Like the gentle but certain structure of the Blues, these techniques lead us always to "Sing to the Lord a New Song."

B. CHORD SYMBOLS

The chord symbols placed at the end of each line at the right hand margin correspond to the chords played in that line. The last chord of the preceeding line is sometimes carried over to the next line without being printed again in the next line. You change chords according to your ear for the music rather than relying on the exact placement of the chord over the syllable where it is supposed to change. Once you know the song, this method will be found to be quite convenient. Most of the chords in this book will be easily understood by guitar players. There are, however, a few which require a a little explanation.

Chords with a "6" after them are major or minor triads with the sixth interval added. For example C6 is composed of the tonic, C, the third interval from the tonic, E, the fifth interval, G, and the sixth, A. Guitar players sometimes know this chord as a 7th of the relative minor; that is, A minor 7th: A, C, E, G, building from the A rather than the C. It is played AEGCG. The relative minor of D is B, and D6 is seen as B minor 7th, played F♯, B, D, A, B, F♯ or the regular B7 chord playing a D natural instead of D sharp. Another variation of the minor 7th chord used in this book is a kind of truncated 9th. In the regular A minor chord we play a B instead of a C by leaving the second string open, playing A, E, A, B, E. This chord has been designated in this book as Am9.

C. MUSICAL REFERENCES

The spiritual richness of American music is dazzling in its diversity: Christian and Jewish, Negro and White, Labor, Civil Rights, Mexican, English, Classical, Rock, Folk, Jazz, Pop, Soul. But a fair sampling of these riches requires recourse to hundreds of publications and almost as many publishers. The inclusion of several hundred currently attractive selections in a volume as small and inexpensive as JTF is therefore no small task.

One of the ways it was done was by eliminating musical notation for songs which seemed either very well known (at least within its class) or of such specialized interest as to warrant reference to specialized collections. Since all of this mu-

sic is intended to be played or sung "by ear," musical notation is unnecessary once the song is known. If the song is not known it can be learned from the noted references to popular recordings, inexpensive collections, or standard works available at most public libraries. Once learned, of course, these too can be played or sung "by ear" like any other.

An important by-product of this economy is that most of the references lead, not simply to the song itself, but to collections of similar music. Thus JTF is more or less open-ended. It is a beginning and each reference serves as an invitation to discover new material. This also eases the pain of editing out material I would like to include, but could not without converting this slim volume into an encyclopedia.

The principal general references together with their letter symbols are as follows:

A   *Alleluia, Hymnbook for Inner City Parishes*, Edited by the Harlem Protestant Parish, 2050 Second Avenue, N.Y., N.Y., Published by Cooperative Recreation Services, Inc., Delaware, Ohio, 75¢.

AFS *Best Loved American Folk Songs (Folk Song, U.S.A.)* by John A. Lomax and Alan Lomax, Grosset and Dunlap, New York, 1947.

EA   *Spiritual Folk Songs of Early America*, George Pullen Jackson, Dover Publications, 180 Varich Street, N.Y., N.Y., $2.00.

F   *Fireside Book of Folk Songs*, by Margaret B. Boni, Simon and Schuster, 1947.

NA   *Folk Songs of North America*, in the English Language by Alan Lomax, Doubleday & Co., N.Y., 1960.

NS   *Books of American Negro Spirituals* by James Weldon Johnson and V. Rosamond Johnson (2 Volumes in 1), Viking Press, N.Y.

PS   *The People's Songbook*, Edited by Waldemar Hille, Oak Publications, 165 W. 46th Street, N.Y., N.Y., 10036, $1.95.

R   *RISK*, Vol. II, No. 3, 1966, published by the Youth Departments of the World Council of Churches and World Council of Christian Education, 150 Route de Ferney, 11211 Geneva 20, Switzerland, 75¢.

SO   *Sing Out*, The Folk Song Magazine, Oak Publications, 165 W. 46th Street, N.Y., N.Y., 10036. Issues $1.00, Reprints (SO no. I through 9R), $1.00.

T   *A Treasury of American Song*, by Olin Downes and Elie Siegmeister, Alfred A. Knopf, 1943.

W   *Travelin On With the Weavers*, Harper & Row, 1966, $2.95.

W&F *Songs of Work and Freedom*, by Edith Fowke and Joe Glazer, Roosevelt University, Chicago, $2.95.

WSO *We Shall Overcome, Songs of the South-*

ern Freedom Movement, by Guy and Candie Carawan for SNCC, Oak Publications, l65 W. 46th Street, N.Y., N.Y., l0036.

Other more specialized references are included in the notes to the numbered songs which follow.

D. NOTES

Chapter 1. MYSTERY, The Call to Freedom

CHANT, ANCIENT
The Meaning of Words

l. The notation is for traditional plainchant according to the eighth psalm tone. The place where the melody goes up is indicated by an accent (Móses, slave, etc.) The syllable on which the melody starts to go down is *italicized.* The time value on each syllable is strictly ad lib. It is never uniform, but follows the natural cadence of ordinary speech. Anything can be sung in chant, including the morning newspaper by simply "pointing" the place where you want to go up and where you come down.

Another ending, known as the second psalm tone, is the same as the eighth shown in the text, but ends this way:

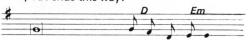

the affliction of my peo*ple* in Egypt
The difference between chanting and reading something is that when you sing them, the words really sink in. Most people can learn the second and eighth psalm tones very easily. They are the ones the monks always sing in the Grade B movies. But they should not be sung like that. They are supposed to swing. The guitar chords shown can help this if the guitarist is respectful of the natural rhythm of the words. We have used Gregorian Chant at rallies accompanied only be a Jazz drummer.

2. c. 1963 by Appleseed Music Inc., All Rights Reserved. Used by permission. R. On the composer's album, "All the News That's Fit to Sing"(Elektra) .

CHANT, AFRICAN
The Personality of Words
3. All the words mean "freedom" except "aiye" which means "world." "Uhuru" is a common salutation in Africa today.
The intimate relationship of words to music as well as the spontaneous nature of good music for a celebration is well illustrated by this chant. I am told by Halim El Dabh of the African Studies Department of Howard University that song making is a very personal thing in Africa; that a visitor is likely to have a song composed on the spot about him, his visit, or any other topic of immediate personal interest. Furthermore, the drums speak too. In fact there is a special "talking" drum which both simulates and accompanies oral speech.

Yet, if many people are to participate, they have to know a little something in advance about what is going to happen.

One way of solving this problem is illustrated here where the leader, following a somewhat familiar pattern, calls out a line and the people repeat it, freely and even with some of their own variations. It is almost impossible to render these personal variations in ordinary music notation. But we can discover some of the basic musical patterns employed. Here is the basic pattern of Uhuru:

Now listen to what happens to this pattern when it is sung by Olatunji and his group (Flaming Drums, Columbia) and with Herbie Mann (The Common Ground, Atlantic)

4. Selections from the Beatles included in JTF are *The Continuing Story of Bungalow Bill* and *Blackbird* both by John Lennon and Paul McCartney, c. 1968. *Within You and Without You* by George Harrison, c. 1967. *She's Leaving Home* and *We Can Work It Out,* both by John Lennon and Paul McCartney, c. 1967. *Eleanor Rigby* by John Lennon and Paul McCartney, c. 1966. *Yesterday, You've Got To Hide Your Love Away, Nowhere Man, Help,* and *The Word,* all by John Lennon and Paul McCartney, c. 1965. All copyrights are held by Northern Songs, Ltd. 71-75 New Oxford Street, London W.C.1, England. Used by Permission. All rights reserved.

WITHIN YOU WITHOUT YOU
One important value of chant is well employed here. Poetic expression is freed from the stricter conventions of rhyme and uniformity in the number of syllables so usually found in the offerings of Tin Pan Alley. This does not mean that this poetry lacks conventions. The convention retained is that of primitive folk song, like the Hebrew's psalms. It is a certain tendency to uniformity in rhythm . Both prose and poetry have rhythm, but the rhythm of prose tends to variety, while that of poetry tends towards uniformity.
5. c. l948 by Tom Glazer, assigned to Songs Music, Inc. Scarborough, N.Y., recorded by Peter, Paul and Mary in their Warner Bros. Album: See What Tomorrow Brings, under the title: Because All Men are Brothers. PS

6s. c.1967 by Louise Ruspini

7s. The "Moses" this song was written about is

Harriet Tubman, an escaped slave who guided thousands of her people to Freedom on the Underground Railroad. A. AFS. F. NS. PS. T., W & F. As recorded on "Life Together." This record, featuring Mother Scott, is part of a book, titled "Communion is Life Together," by Rosemary Reuther, Herder & Herder, 232 Madison Avenue, NYC 10016 ($1.25 children's edition; $1.95 parent's edition with record)

THE CERTAIN BEAT

The two-part arrangement in Spirituals for City People is the same as on the record. It is discordant,   and unlike the usual concert or choral "performances" of this great people's song, it maintains a steady beat throughout. African drums were used on the recording.

It is a near absolute requirement for group singing that a regular and distinct rhythm be maintained at all times. Retards and accelerations of tempo may be dramatic for solo work where the singing is *for* someone; but a song leader is not supposed to sing *for* people. He is supposed to sing *with* people. His success is measured, not by the beauty of his voice, but by his ability to get people to enter into the spirit of the song and join together on the chorus. There is a whole philosophy of social leadership built into this singing approach which would be very worthwhile considering. As this song and arrangement illustrate, social singing style is not simplistic "sing along" music. It is very sophisticated.

8s. Sing it like A—BELA—CHOW!

9s. The hard questions are not anti-religious. They are from the Bible: Habakkuk, Isaiah, Jeremiah, and St. John (Revelation).

10s. c. 1965 by Patrick Mason, as recorded by the composer, Chiro Record Co., 1210 W. Boston Blvd., Detroit, Michigan.

Not all songs have to be sung in whole or in part by the people at a celebration. This song is a good example of a song to be listened to. The response is still there, though unsung.

11. As recorded by the Kinks. c. American Metropolitan Enterprises of New York, Inc.

12. c.1963 by Appleseed Music, Inc.   Used by Permission. All Rights Reserved. SO9R. As sung on album Phil Ochs in Concert (Elektra).

13s. c.1965 by the Youth Department, The American Lutheran Church, 422 Fifth Street, Minneapolis 15, Minn. R.

14. c. Gypsy Boy Music, 1966. As recorded by composer on album, Little Wheel Spin and Spin (Vanguard).

15. c. 1963 by Sydney Carter. See Note 17s.

JOE HILL

16S. To be played and sung a little differently than the music usually says.   It needs a ¾ time "street-corner beat."   Joe Hill was the poet laureate of the International Workers of the World, the IWW, or "Wobblies," a native grass roots radical movement in the United States in the early part of this century. In 1915 Joe Hill was executed by a firing squad in Salt Lake City. His last words to the IWW became famous: "Don't waste time mourning. Organize." His ashes were scattered on every continent, but no ashes were dropped in Utah because Joe "didn't want to be found dead there." Further on Joe Hill see W&F and listen to Joe Glazer on Songs of Joe Hill (Folkways)

17S. c. 1965 by Sydney Carter. From "10 New Songs by Sydney Carter," Clarion Photographic Services, Ltd., 21 Greek Street, London, W.1. ($1). Listen to recording on "Life Together." See Note 7S. The adaptation and arrangement included here is with permission. It is the same as on the record and calls for a Bosa Nova beat.

18S. c. 1964, Ryerson Music Publishers. Used by Permission. All Rights Reserved. Recorded by Joan Baez, Vanguard 79160. The musical arrangement included here is somewhat different.

19.   John Borger wrote out the guitar chords for inclusion in the text and then crossed them out. "You either know how to play the blues or you don't, and if you don't there is nothing we can do about it in this book." Listen to the composer sing and play them on "Everybody's Got A Right to Live" Broadside Records, 701 Seventh Avenue, N.Y., N.Y. Other songs by Rev. Kirkpatrick in JTF in addition to "Cities are Burnin" are "Everybody's Got a Right to Live," "You're Just a Laughin' Fool" all copyright 1968 by Frederick Douglass Kirkpatrick. Also included from the same album is "Burn, Baby, Burn" by Jimmy Collier, c. 1966. See also the July 1966 issue of Sing Out which carries the song and a story about Jimmy Collier.

20. c.1964 Burlington Music Co., Ltd. London, England.   Published   by   Frank Music Corp. 119 W.57th St., NYNY by arrangement   with Burlington Music Corp.   The Album is Pata Pata (Reprise).

PADRAIC PEARCE

21.   Padraic Pearce was the leader of the Irish Easter Rebellion in 1916.   His works are variously published.

22. c. 1968 by Joyful Wisdom. The record is Feel Like I'm Fixin' To Die (Vanguard).

23.   Record of songs and sounds from the Delano strike has been released by the farm workers themselves ($4.25). Thunderbird Records, Box 1060, Delano, Calif. See also SO, Nov. 1966.

24S. The words are from Psalms 84, 85, 105 and Isaiah 61.

25. c. 1961 by Sydney Carter from "9 Carols or Ballads by Sydney Carter." See note 17S.

REPEAT, REPEAT

26S. This song carries the call and repeat idea of Uhuru (Note 3) just about as far as it will go.   The last three lines always remain the same. WSO.

27. c. 1965, Miriam Therese Winter. As re-

corded on album, Joy is Like the Rain (Avant Garde)

28S. W&F

CHANT WITH A LITTLE MORE STRUCTURE
29S. c. 1969 by John Snyder. In this contemporary adaptation of "Tone De Bell Easy" or "Jesus Gonna Make Up My Dyin' Bed" (American Ballads and Folk Songs by John A. and Alan Lomax, Macmillan, 1934) we see chant endings in the verse similar to those of Gregorian Chant. Compare the endings below "to set men free," "us all to liberty," with the kind of endings discussed in note I, supra. But here these endings are preceded by phrases which have a uniform number of stressed syllables See, infra, note 31.

Well well well! Who's that a callin'

Well well well! Take your neighbor's hand

Well well well! Daylight's a dawnin'

Cause the spirit is movin' all over the land

The spirit is movin' to set men free

The spirit is callin' us all to liberty

Brothers and sisters side by side

all standin' up and they won't hide

30. ROCKIN' JERUSALEM (page 14). This adaptation of the traditional spiritual (Cf. choral arrangement by John W. Work, Theodore Presser Co., Bryn Mawr, Pennsylvania and recording by Fisk Jubilee Singers directed by Mr. Work [Folkways]) is intended to be sung by three groups of people at once. The first line is started by one group. As they continue, a second group comes in with the second line and as both groups continue, a third group or a soloist sings the third line. It ends by tapering

off till only the first group is left. The words of this first line lay down a strong rhythmic pattern on which the rest builds. It is good a capella, or with a jazz accompaniment. The Fm7 is an intentional dischord.

Chapter 2. FEAR, The Urge to Run Away
METRICAL CHANT

31. This kind of chant depends on the poetry having a regular number of stressed syllables in each line. Each of the four lines in the text of the psalm at the beginning of this chapter has three stressed syllables. That's where the chord and melody lines change in the following metrical chant pattern:

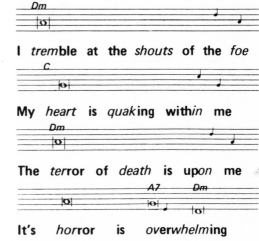

I *trem*bel **at the** *shouts* **of the** *foe*

My *heart* **is** *quak*ing **with**in **me**

The *terror* **of** *death* **is** up*on* **me**

It's *horror* **is** *overwhelm*ing

The small notes indicate possible but nonessential melodic options.

METRICAL CHANT
AND ANTIPHONAL SINGING

Ever since Miriam led the girls in song at the party they had after Pharoah's army got drowned, antiphonal singing—where the people respond with a simple refrain to verses sung by a leader—has been a favorite form of social singing. One of its big advantages is that people don't have to look at books while they're singing, and that always makes for a better party. This kind of singing largely shaped the musical form of American Negro spirituals and revival hymns.

Many songs in JTF readily lend themselves to this type of singing. Wherever possible the antiphonal style should be employed since it is more interesting and more liberating. Most of the music in JTF of this type is simple enough for an untutored leader to call out the verses for the people to repeat or answer with a refrain. More extended verses such as those designated here as metrical chants require the leader to develop some skills. They are not difficult, but they require some thought, some listening and some practice.

MELODY AND RHYTHM
Aid to Meaning

As we said earlier in talking about a contemporary chant of the Beatles (Note 4), both prose and poetry have ryhthm. But the rhythm of prose tends to variety while that of poetry tends toward uniformity. There is no definite dividing line, and no technical measure.

Live poetry seldom matches the artificial scansion patterns we learned in school. Hamlet's famous soliloquy is theoretically in iambic pentameter; that is, each line is made up of five "iambs" (an accented syllable preceded by an unaccented one). Read strictly, according to bookish scansion, the lines would be abysmal singsong:

To 'be or not to be, that is the question.

Read naturally, so as to convey meaning, the scansion would be more like:

To be or not to be, that is the question.

But this rendering has only four accented syllables and only two of them iambic. In reading, therefore, and particularly in singing, we must be careful to speak the words naturally— as if they were unpatterned prose. To help the singer concentrate on meaning, and give a personal rendering, stressed syllables have not been marked off in this book except in a few cases where the purpose is illustration. This fact may, at first, seem a handicap in keeping a steady "beat." But once the melodic and rhythmic patterns of the chant becomes familiar, it will be easy enough. The rhythm will be freer because choice of the stressed syllable is left to the natural flow of the singer's speech rather than to someone else's selection.

A song leader must **sing** on key, hit his notes fair and square (no scooping and sliding) and project. He has to be heard clearly. The words have to come through. But otherwise, voice quality does not enter into the equation. In fact, a "beautiful" voice can be a handicap in eliciting a group response. People may get the impression it's a one-man show and just listen. But, whatever your voice quality, if the words come through wrapped in your personality without any obvious musical flaw, you will be an effective song leader.

MORE METRICAL CHANTS

Here are a few more metrical chants which you can use with any verses in this book noted 31. All poetry so marked has four lines with three stressed syllables in each. Sometimes the lines, because of their length, may run to more than four lines in the printing, but the meter is the same and easily discoverable.

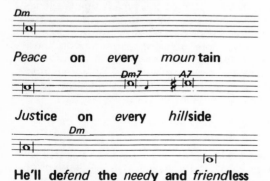

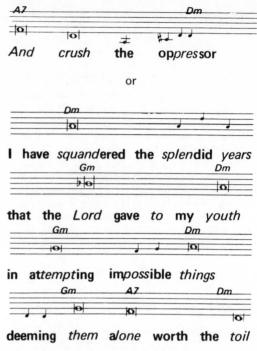

Occasionally, the poetry ends with only two lines. In this event you merely repeat the pattern of the last two lines of the four line stanza. Thus:

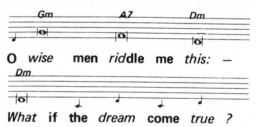

Two line endings like this can also be used as antiphons.

Most of the chant patterns here can be easily adapted to poetry with a greater or lesser number of stressed syllables per line so that almost any poetry in this book can be sung. Other metrical chants are included under notes 29, 38, 42, 69, 111, 118 and 151.

ANTIPHONS

The obvious antiphon for the verses from Psalm 55 at the beginning of Chapter 2 is the song at the end, "Where You Gonna Run To," note 40S. In all cases, the chant takes its rhythm from the antiphon. Other song refrains suitable for antiphons to metrical chants, and in the same key, D Minor, are as follows: |Jonah, n. 13S, Rockin' Jerusalem, p. 14, A New People, p. 41, Lonesome Traveller, n. 87S, Which Side Are You On, n. 111S, Send Forth Your Spirit, p. 69, Precious Death, n. 132, The Great Hallelu. n. 151, Hiney Matov, n. 157S, and, in other keys, Gonna Sing My Lord, n.

Seek and You Shall Find, n. 58S, Shalom Alechem, n. 155S; also, possibly, some of the refrains to other chants, n. 29, n. 38, n.42, p. 51, n. 118, and many others.

32. A talk in Houston, Texas, 1966, Worship in the City of Man, The Liturgical Conference, Washington, D.C.

33. c. 1962 by Schroeder Music Co.from"Little Boxes and other Homemade Songs" by Malvina Reynolds. Oak Publications 165 W. 46th St., NYNY 20036. $2.45.

34. c. 1966 by Deep Fork Music, Inc. Used by Permission. All Rights Reserved. As recorded by the composer on album, Morning After (Elektra).

35. c. 1966 by Fall River Music, Inc. Used by Permission. All rights reserved. Broadside magazine #67, 215 W. 98th St. NYC.

36. c. 1964, 1966 Ryerson Music Pub., Inc. Used by Permission. All Rights Reserved. As recorded by Richard and Mimi Farina on album, Celebrations for a Gray Day, (Vanguard).

37. Compare the version in the text with Mahalia Jackson's version on album, Mahalia Jackson, The World's Greatest Gospel Singer (Columbia).

38. c. 1969 by Ozzie Gontang and Landon Dowdey. Another chant with a different number of stressed syllables to the line.

Polite *smiles.***Good** *man***ners.Pleasant** *talk*

Be*long***ing to all the** *in* **groups.** *Do***ing all**

the *right* **things.** *Dy***ing.** *Dy***ing.** *Dy***ing.**

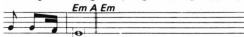

Afraid **to** *live*

39. c. 1965 by Deep Fork Music, Inc. Used by Permission. All rights reserved. SO April-May, 1966. Recorded by composer in album Ain't That News (Elektra).
40s.

Chapter 3. COURAGE, Responding to the Risk

41. Listen to Ramsey Lewis album of same title (Cadet). Cf. NS (God is Gonna Trouble the Water) and NA.

GEORGE FOX

42. George Fox, who may have resembled some contemporary protestors, was the 17th century founder of the Society of Friends. He was frequently jailed for saying the things expressed so well in these verses by Sydney Carter, c. 1964. See note 17S. These verses, very good in the English Folk Song setting of the composer (See his 9 Carols or Ballads), are also ideally suited to an antiphonal style. The power of the poetry can be brought out in the more personalized singing of a leader with the people affirming what he says by joining in on the chorus. John Borger and I fitted the following chant and refrain to Sydney Carter's text.

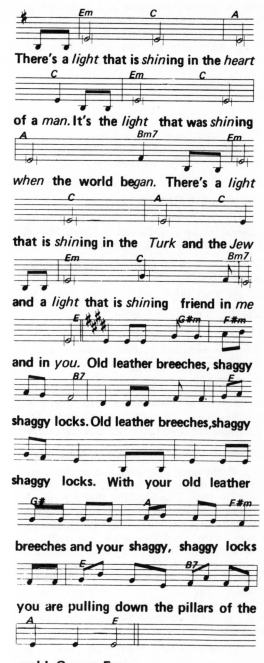

There's a *light* **that is** *shin***ing in the** *heart*

of a *man.***It's the** *light* **that was** *shin***ing**

when **the world be***gan.* **There's a** *light*

that is *shin***ing in the** *Turk* **and the** *Jew*

and a *light* **that is** *shin***ing friend in** *me*

and in *you.* **Old leather breeches, shaggy**

shaggy locks. Old leather breeches,shaggy

shaggy locks. With your old leather

breeches and your shaggy, shaggy locks

you are pulling down the pillars of the

world, George Fox.

43. c. 1946 Ludlow Music, Inc. NY. "Woodie Guthrie, American Folk Songs," Edited by Moses Asch, Oak Publications, $1.95, W&F, PS.

44S. See note 19.

45. WSO, PS.

46S. Cf. WSO and Mahalia Jackson's "Keep Your Hand on the Plow" on her album, The Greatest Gospel Singer (Columbia).

47. c. 1969 Build Black, Inc. If you're not hip, "rap" means talk and "suds" means beer, a perfect formula for getting at the truth. At these weekly sessions in the riot-torn areas of upper Cardoza in Washington, people who never made speeches before got up and said to their neighbors things that they had never before been able to say to themselves. The truth was not pretty, but it was beautiful. Build Black, 3320 14th St., NW, Washington, D.C. plans to issue a record of these sessions soon.

47S. A, PS.

48. Cf. SO 6R.

49S. c. 1966 by Rev. Antonio Gonzalez, OMI.

50. c. 1967, World Library Publications, Inc. Cincinnati, Ohio, 45214, from whom the record and songbook (35¢) are available.

51. A, WSO, W&F.

52S. Cf. WSO, SO # 7R.

53. Cf. W&F, WSO, PS. Read about Harriet Tubman in Lerone Bennett's Negro History, Before The Mayflower (Pelican).

54. A. As sung by Mother Scott on "Life Together." See Note 7S.

55. PS, WSO, W&F.

56S. Cf. "I'm So Glad" WSO.

57S.

58S. As recorded by Pete Seeger on album, Waist Deep in Big Muddy (Columbia).

59. Note omitted.

60. c. 1963 SFO Music, Inc. 916 Kearny St., San Francisco. Recorded by Kingston Trio, Jefferson Airplane Takes Off and many others

Chapter 4. LOVE, The Reason for the Journey

61. Really good love songs and stories are significantly rare in our culture. This old one from the Bible is so beautiful that it turns a lot of church people off. The chant is simple for people to follow. The melody always goes down on the italicized syllable, and it all starts over again with each paragraph. When John Snyder and his bride Jane got married, everybody in church sang this after the briefest rehearsal. The men sang the Groom's part, the women the Bride's, and all together on the Chorus. c. 1968 by Ozzie Gontang and Landon Dowdey.

62. c. 1963 (unpub), 1964, 1965 Cherry Lane Music, Inc. Used by Permission. All rights reserved. "Ramblin' Boy and Other Songs" by Tom Paxton, Oak Publications $2.45. W.

63. c. 1965. by Stormking Music, Inc. All Rights Reserved. Used by Permission. As recorded by composer on album, Strangers and Cousins (Columbia)

OLD BOOKS

64S. Another love song from the Bible. What most people overlook about this book is that it is folk literature: songs, stories, history, customs, laws, and even self criticism. The words in the first few stanzas of our adaptation of this American folk hymn are little changed from the original, showing that the simple folk in America understood very well what the simple folk of Israel were talking about when they wrote down this story about 3,000 years ago. "In the days before newspapers, and among people who couldn't have read them even if they had existed, the folk song was a kind of chronicle and running commentary on the times. Many of them have lived for hundreds of years, while nothing is more dead than yesterday's newspapers. The folk songs and story ballads were not the most accurate kind of history of course, because once the event, whatever it was, had been recorded, generations of singers went on elaborating and changing the song— smoothing it out, or shaping it up to suit their own ideas of how the event might have happened. Often, the event which started the song was blurred or lost as time went on. The song then took on its own independent life. Aristotle said in his poetics that art is truer than history because it shows what should have happened rather than simply what did happen. It is true to its own inner necessity rather than the accidental historical event. In this sense the song is certainly true, because however much the actual event which inspired the song might be changed, the song was always a true record of attitudes and feelings of the generation." (Cisco Houston, A Legacy, Folkways) c. 1968 by Ozzie Gontang and Landon Dowdey.

65.   omitted

66. c. 1958 & 1963 Ludlow Music, Inc. NYC. Used by Permission. W, WSO, "Life Together" Note 7S.

67. Cf. W

68. c. 1959 by Stormking Music Inc. All Rights Reserved. Used by Permission. SO 2R. As recorded by composer on album, Strangers and Cousins (Columbia).

69. c. 1968 by John Snyder and Landon Dowdey. This song (like this whole chapter) can be applied with equal force to both the intimate love relationships of a man and woman as well as to societal relationships generally. This is not necessarily an idea which originated with Freud. In World War I, the following order issued from General Pershing's Headquarters in France:

"Make a point of keeping the native cantonment population from spoiling the Negroes. Americans become greatly incensed at any public expression of intimacy between white women and black men."

Lerone Bennett, Jr. observed

"Sin. Sex. Race. The three words took deep roots, intertwined and became one in the Puritan psyche."

Chapter 5. SORROW, The Loneliness of Captivity

70. AFS, NS.

71.   AFS, F, NA, PS. As recorded by Cisco Houston on album, A Legacy (Folkways).

72S. NA. See A Thousand Years of Irish Poetry by Kathleen Hoagland, Devon-Adair, 1947.

73. Omitted   74. Omitted

75.   c. 1962 by Fall River Music Inc. All Rights Reserved. Used by Permission.

76. Omitted   77. R.   78S. Cf. NS.

79. Cf. R. A Calypso style. Each succeeding pair of verses is sung on the same melodic line as the first pair for which the notation is given here, due care being taken for the natural rhythm of the words. It can be sung with a leader doing the verse and the group on refrain or the group doing the whole thing. Drums help.

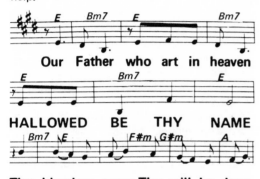

Our Father who art in heaven

HALLOWED   BE   THY   NAME

Thy kingdom come. Thy will be done.

HALLOWED   BE   THY   NAME

80S. Cf. EA. 81. Omitted

82. W. As recorded by the Poso Seco Singers on album, Time I'll Be Gone (Columbia).

83S. Cf. NS. As recorded on Odetta at the Gate of Horn (Tradition).

Chapter 6. CHANGE, The Road of Promise

84. c. 1965 by M.J. Archer and A.D. Rosetti.

85.   c. 1962 by Fall River Music Inc. All Rights Reserved. Used by Permission. SO#8R. As recorded by Pete Seeger on album, I Can See a New Day (Columbia).

86S. c. 1967 by John Snyder.

87. Recorded on The Weavers at Carnegie Hall (Vanguard VRS 9010).

88. cf. PS, W&F. 89s.   90s.

91. c. 1962, 1964, 1965 by Cherry Lane Music, Inc. Used by permission. All rights reserved. As recorded on Ramblin' Boy (Elektra).

92S. Adaptation of Shaker hymn by Victor Ferkiss and Landon Dowdey. The melody was used by Aaron Copeland in his Appalachian Spring Suite. It is heard in a more stately form as the theme of a well known TV news program. But the original is lively. An important part of Shaker asceticism was dancing, and they marked this one "Shaker allegro." This and other Shaker hymns and history can be found in THE GIFT TO BE SIMPLE by Edward Deming Andrews, Dover Publications, 180 Varich Street, N.Y., N.Y. ($1.50). The Shakers were by far the most successful American experiment in communal living; and but for another aspect of their asceticism—celibacy—they would probably still be around.

93S. Cf. A, NS.

94. c. 1961 by Sydney Carter. See Note 17S.

95. An important organizational effort of the Wobblies (see Note 16S) was among farm workers. Because of repression, it was clandestine and included industrial sabotage. The early version of this song given here is fairly rare. After the Labor Movement got better organized, it dropped talk about industrial sabatoge. So this song became "Boom Went the Boom"—meaning 1929. Although everyone knows about the ways of power it's unmentionable in public. As Charles S. Johnson says about the leader of an early slave uprising:

"Vesey represents the spirit of independence for which the founding fathers of America are praised—an insurrection is merely an unsuccessful revolution. But Denmark Vesey is a symbol of a spirit too violent to be acceptable to the white community. There are no Negro schools named for him, and it would be extremely poor taste and bad judgment for the Negroes to take any pride in his courage and philosophy. There is, indeed, little chance for Negro youth to know about him at all."

96S. Cf. O'Donnell Abu in Irish Songs of Resistance by Patrick Galvan, Oak. Further on Jim Connell who also composed the official song of the British Labor Party, "The Red Flag," see W&F. Also, A Thousand Years of Irish Poetry by Kathleen Hoagland, Devon Adair, 1947.

97. Cf.NA   98. See Note 19.

99. c. 1965 by East Publications, Inc.

100. c. 1962 by Melody Trails, Inc. Used By Permission. SO #9R. As recorded by the Byrds (Columbia).   101S. Cf. WSO.

Chapter 7. STRUGGLE, Participate in the Journey

WAKE UP

Cf. Isaiah 51, 52, 60, 61; Psalm 113; Romans 13, 11-14. The basic chant, "Wake Up! Rise Up!" etc. lays down a strong rhythmic figure which can be reinforced with hand-clapping, drums or bass. After the group is moving with this, the verses (italicized) can be interjected by the leader. This chant is also good without any musical accompaniment.

THAT "OLD TIME RELIGION"

The words and theme of the opening chant of this chapter, although often repeated in the

Bible, are usually identified by the public with "Godless Communism." But our religion of conformity was a problem long before Marx was mentioned on this side of the ocean. In a postscript to his famous Narrative, Frederick Douglass takes note of possible misinterpretation of seemingly anti-religious statements in his book:

"Between the Christianity of this land, and the Christianity of Christ, I recognize the widest possible difference. I can see no reason, but the most deceitful one, for calling the religion of this land Christianity. I look upon it as the climax of all misnomers, the boldest of all frauds, and the grossest of all libels."

Perhaps the worst of all the libels is the preaching of the passive submission to oppressed people in an ever changing variety of forms by the American Church. Professor DuBois (Souls of Black Folk) describes the consequences:

"This deep religious fatalism, painted so beautifully in "Uncle Tom," came soon to breed, as all fatalistic faiths will, the sensualist side by side with the martyr. Under the lax moral life of the plantation, where marriage was a farce, laziness a virtue, and property a theft, a religion of resignation and submission degenerated easily, in less strenuous minds, into a philosophy of indulgence and crime. Many of the worst characteristics of the Negro masses of to-day had their seed in this period of the slave's ethical growth. Here it was that the Home was ruined under the very shadow of the Church, white and black; here habits of shiftlessness took root, and sullen hopelessness replaced hopeful strife."

And he prescribes the remedy:

"With the beginning of the abolition movement and the gradual growth of a class of free Negroes came a change. Freedom became to him a real thing and not a dream. His religion became darker and more intense, and into his ethics crept a note of revenge, into his songs a day of reckoning close at hand. The "Coming of the Lord" swept this side of Death, and came to be a thing to be hoped for in this day. The black bards caught new notes, and sometimes even dared to sing,—
"O Freedom, O Freedom
O Freedom over me!
Before I'll be a slave
I'll be buried in my grave
And go home to my Lord
And be free."

102. c. 1964 by Schroeder Music Company. SO #9R. As recorded on Judy Collins' Fifth Album (Elektra).

This is a very American song. As Justice Louis Brandeis said in a Supreme Court opinion in 1927 (Whitney v. California, 274 US 357), "Those who won our independence by revolution were not cowards. They did not fear po-

litical change. They did not exalt order at the cost of liberty."

103. c. 1961 and 1963 by Ludlow Music Inc. Used by Permission. SO #9R. As recorded by Cisco Houston (Vanguard).

104S. Cf. The Songs We Sing by Harry Coopersmith, United Synagogue Commission on Jewish Education, 1950. F.   105. WSO.

106S. c.1969 by Ann Marie McLoone 107. PS.

108S. c. 1968 by Mother Scott.

109. c. 1957 and 1965 by Ludlow Music, Inc. New York, New York. Used by Permission. As recorded on Best of Oscar Brand (Tradition).

110. W&F. Merle Travis' original recording of Sixteen Tons on album, Back Home (Capitol T-891).

111. Cf. W&F, WSO. We have a simpler chant version.

112. W&F. An earlier version of Son of a Gambolier is found in Carl Sandburg's American Song Bag, Harcourt Brace & Co., New York, 1927.

113. W&F. As sung by Oscar Brand. Recorded on album, Best of Oscar Brand (Tradition).

114. PS .   115. W&F.   116. Cf. WSO

117S. The tune is the old white spiritual, "Amazing Grace." AFS, EA, W. Recorded on the Weavers at Carnegie Hall, v. 2 (Vanguard VRS 9075 & VSD 2069).

Chapter 8. HELP, The Weary Traveler

118. c. 1969 by John Snyder and Landon Dowdey. Cf. NA, N.S. and record by Big Brother and the Holding Company

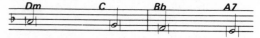

*Been **travelin'** round a jumbled up world*

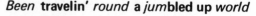

It's *hard* to *see* what I *see*

People aren't *movin'* just *driftin'* around

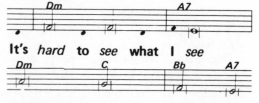

Don't *know* what *they* want to *be*

The blind man stood in the road and cried

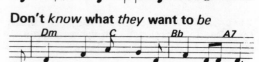

The blind man stood in the road and cried

The blind man stood in the road and cried

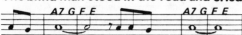

Crying Oh . . . Show me the way . . .

119. c. 1965 Deep Fork Music, Inc. Used by Permission. All Rights Reserved. As recorded by Eric Anderson on Album 'Bout Changes 'N Things (Vanguard).

120. The theme song of the Mississippi Summer Project after the disappearance of Goodman, Schwerner, and Chaney. Cf. SOR#9. The following adaptation is to be sung slowly and deliberately with a driving rock.

121S. A, WSO. In the Narrative of his life, Frederick Douglass says:

"I have often been utterly astonished, since I came to the north, to find persons who could speak of the singing, among slaves, as evidence of their contentment and happiness. It is impossible to conceive of a greater mistake. Slaves sing most when they are most unhappy. The songs of the slave represent the sorrows of his heart; and he is relieved by them, only as an aching heart is relieved by its tears. . . . The singing of a man cast away upon a desolate island might be as appropriately considered as evidence of contentment and happiness. as the singing of a slave; the songs of the one and of the other are prompted by the same emotion."
And see also in W.E.B. DuBois, Souls of Black Folk, the moving chapter on the "Sorrow Songs."

Listen to this song on album, Freedom Singers Sing Freedom Now (1964 SNCC Convention in Atlanta), Mercury.

122. A, NS. We like this in a rolling rock style. That's why the guitar chords are pat-terned this way.

123. c. 1964 by Appleseed Music Inc. All Rights Reserved. SO. V. 15#4. As recorded by Pete Seeger on album, I Can See a New Day, Columbia.

Chapter 9. SUFFERING, The Cost of Travel

124. c. 1968 by John Borger and Landon Dowdey.

125. A, NS.

126. c. 1961 and 1963 by Ludlow Music Inc. Used by Permission. SO #4R. As sung by Cisco Houston (Vanguard).

127. The music and record are available from Stimuli, Inc., 17 Erkenbrecher Ave., Cincinnati, Ohio 45220.

128. See note 23.   129. A, AFS, EA.

130. c. 1959 by Ludlow Music Inc., N.Y.,N.Y. See note 23. PS, W&F, WSO.

131. c. 1924 by H.A. Percy. See recording of The Rejoice Mass (General Theological Seminary) Scepter.

132.

Precious in the sight of the Lord

is the death of his friends.

133S. See discussion of this song in W.E.B. DuBois, The Souls of Black Folk.

134S. c.1969, Rev. E. Briere, Madonna House, Cumbermere, Ontario.

135. WSO. As sung by Freedom Singers Sing Freedom Now (Mercury)

Chapter 10. CREATION, Marriage to Life

137. A.

138. c. 1960 by Sanga Music Inc. All Rights Reserved. Used by Permission. W. As recorded by The Weavers.

139. Recorded by Harry Belafonte, on album, An Evening with Belafonte (RCA Victor).

140. F, NA. 141S. Cf. A, SO#R. 142. Cf.WSO.

143. Cf. A, F, NA, NS. 144S. Cf. A, NS, WSO.

145. Recorded on The Weavers at Carnegie Hall (Vanguard VRS 9010).

146S.   147. SO, July 1965.   148S.

Chapter 11. THE KINGDOM,
A Free Community

149S.

150. c. 1961 and 1963 by Ludlow Music Inc., N.Y.,N.Y. Used By Permission. SO#1R.

151.

He *raises* **the** *poor* **from the** *dust.* **From**

the *gar*bage **heap he** *lifts* **up the** *low*ly.

Sing out the great hallayloo! Hallay!

Hallaylooyah! Hallay! Hallayloo!

152. W&F. See Note 23.

153S. c. 1969 by Joe Glazer.   154. W&F.
154S.   See also "God's Goin' to Set This
World on Fire" an old Wobblie version in Carl
Sandburg's American Song Bag.

155S. It means a lot more than "hello" or
"good-bye" or the usual translation "peace be
to you." These words Jesus spoke so often in
the Bible mean not simply non-violence; they
convey a notion of sharing oneself with another.

156. AE. 157. Cf. W.   158S. SO #9R.
159s. The tune is "Amen" from *Lilies of the
Field.* A. WSO.R.

160S. "Peace" or "Sharing" (see note 155),
Havayreem, "my friends " R.   Recorded on
The Weavers' Reunion at Carnegie Hall, PartII
(Vanguard VRS 9161 & VSD 79161).

161. A, NA. Recorded on Mahalia Jackson,
The World's Greatest Gospel Singer (Columbia).
If you have some doubts about the connection
between Jazz and Spirituals, this recording
ought to end them.
162. c. 1969 by Mother Scott

E. SPIRITUALS FOR CITY PEOPLE

It is more than coincidental that the religious
music of the masses—the music we like to sing
when we're not in church–happens to come
from the poor churches of America: the Negro spirituals of the South, the White spirituals of Appalachia and the West, and the Gospel
blues of our cities.

By excluding this music from their hymnals,
the more respectable churches have made God
over into their own image. Like the Indian
who went to the white man's church and then
dreamed of dying and going to heaven. He
could not remember exactly how God looked,
but he seemed to resemble in appearance and
dress a successful American businessman. He
was in an office-like room, seated behind a
desk, "just like a bank." (American Indian

Prose and Poetry, edited by Margot Astrov,
Capricorn Books Edition, 1962)

It is startling to hear a Jazz Mass in German
("Freut Euch Der Herr Ist Nah" AMS Studio
15009–L. Schwann, Dusseldorf). At first it
sounds a bit disengenuous to hear "Go Tell It
On the Mountain" sung by a German congregation. But that is because we do not realize the
extent to which popular music throughout the
world has been influenced by American Jazz
and other contemporary derivations of the Negro spiritual. It has bridged all cultural, ideo-
logical, and political barriers to become the
rage of the Soviet Union. Listen to a popular
foreign radio station sometime.   How can
church music be called American when it fails
to accord a substantial place to our one inter-
nationally recognized cultural contribution?

In selecting and adapting music for Journey to
Freedom, and especially for the supplement,
Spirituals for City People, we looked to this
great Black American musical tradition. We
looked to other rich cultural strains also: Appalachian, Jewish and Spanish. But honesty
requires the collection weigh most heavily on
the Black side because that is, preeminently,
the color of American music.

Our adaptations and arrangements will un-
doubtedly offend the antiquarians and purists.
But we are not aiming at singing "Old Slave
Songs" the way they used to sing them on the
"Old Plantation." That kind of nostalgia for
rural ways, so manifest in our flight to the suburbs, period architecture, etc., is a big part of
America's problem. It is one of the ways we
escape from the realities of a society which is
becoming more urbanized each day.

Still it is hoped that Journey to Freedom
and the musical adaptations and arrangements
here in Spirituals for City People meet the
broader aspirations of Professor George Pullen
Jackson in his classic work, Spiritual Folk
Songs of Early America (1937, Dover Edition
1964): "The lore of a folk comprehends, as I
understand it, the whole of its basic cultural
accomplishments. [And in the American melt-
ing pot that includes a zestful variety!] Understood in this broadest and deepest sense, a folk-
lore is truer, more vital and more significant
than an art lore. It is a clearer mirror of a people's past, a more reliable interpreter of its present trends, and a safer prophet of its culture to
come. It is all of this because it is the body and
soul of that culture, where art is merely a vest-
ment. The art which fits best this body and
soul, this basic ethnic character, is the best art.
The art of ancient Greece was great for this
reason. All students of aesthetics since Lessing
and Winkelmann have recognized this. They
have recognized also that the great periods in
the art of any enduring people are those when
its gifted creators act in closest harmony with
the genius of their race; and that its barren
periods are those when the masters have been
faithless to their own and have sought afar 'the
good which lies so near.' "

28. WE'RE GONNA ROLL

40. WHERE YOU GONNA RUN TO?

44. LAUGHIN' FOOL

46. KEEP YOUR EYE ONE THE PRIZE

47. MARY DON'T YOU WEEP

49. JUSTICIA EN MARCHA

52. WOKE UP THIS MORNIN'

56. SEIZE JOY

57. LA BAMBA

111. WHICH SIDE ARE YOU ON?

117. AMAZING LOVE

121. COME BY HERE

133. MICHAEL HAUL YOUR BOAT ASHORE

134. THOSE WHO SOW IN SORROW

141. GO TELL IT ON THE MOUNTAIN

143. RISE UP SHEPHERD

144. I WANT TO BE READY

146. DE COLORES

F. SELECT BIBLIOGRAPHY

Margot Astrov, *American Indian Prose and Poetry,* Capricorn Books Edition, New York, New York, 1962.

James Baldwin, *Nobody Knows My Name,* Dell, New York, New York.

Sarah Zweig Betsky, *Onions and Cucumbers and Plums, 46 Yiddish Poems in English,* Wayne State University Press, Detroit, Michigan, 1958.

Lerone Bennett, Jr., *Before the Mayflower,* Johnson Publishing Company, 1962. Paperback edition by Pelican, Penguin.

Eldridge Cleaver, *Soul on Ice,* McGraw Hill, Inc., New York, New York, 1968.

Frederick Douglass, *Narrative of the Life of Frederick Douglass, an American Slave,* written by himself, Harvard University Press, Boston, 1960. Paperback edition by same.

W.E.B. DuBois, *Souls of Black Folk,* Chicago, 1903. Paperback edition by Fawcett World.

Erich Fromm, *The Sane Society,* 1955, Rinehart and Company, New York, New York; concerning Ritual, see pp. 144-146, 347-352, and see also the parent work, *Escape From Freedom,* 1941, Holt Rinehart and Winston.

Corita Kent, *Footnotes and Headlines,* Herder and Herder, New York, New York, 1967.

Kathleen Hoagland, *A Thousand Years of Irish Poetry,* Devon-Adair, 1947.

Martin Luther King, Jr., *Why We Can't Wait,* New York, 1964. Records: *Martin Luther King at Zion Hill; Martin Luther King, The American Dream,* Dooto Records, 13440 South Central Avenue, Los Angeles, California 90059; *The Great March on Washington,* and *The Great March To Freedom, Martin Luther King,* Detroit, June 12, 1963, Gordy, a division of Motown Record Corporation.

Autobiography of Malcolm X, Grove Press, N.Y.N.Y. 1964. (Paperback). Listen to the famous "Ballots or Bullets" speech on First Amendment Records, Jamie Fuyden Distributing Corporation, 919 N. Broad St., Philadelphia, Pa. 19123; also *Message to the Grass Roots,* Grass Roots L.P. Company, 14951 Schaefer Rd., Detroit, Michigan.

Maria Montessori, *The Montessori Method,* 1912; Schocken Edition, 1964, New York, New York; *The Secret of Childhood,* Orient Longmans, Bombay, India, 1936.

Boris Pasternak, *Doctor Zhivago,* Pantheon Books, a division of Random House, New York, New York, 1958.

Carl Sandburg, *Cornhuskers; Chicago Poems,* Holt, Rinehart & Winston, New York, New York.

Robert Theobald, *An Alternative Future for America,* Swallow Press, 1968 ($1.95) both about and by a Free University.

Tennessee Williams, ' "The Glass Menagerie," Random House, New York, New York; "The Rose Tattoo," "Battle of the Angels," "Orpheus Descending" and "Camino Real," New Directions Publishing Corporation, New York, New York.

CREDITS AND ACKNOWLEDGEMENTS

Grateful acknowledgement is made for the use of excerpts from the following copyrighted materials:

Soul On Ice, c. 1968 by Eldridge Cleaver. Published by McGraw Hill. Used by Permission. All Rights Reserved.

Footnotes and Headlines by Corita Kent, c. 1967 by Herder and Herder. Used by Permission. All Rights Reserved.

Doctor Zhivago by Boris Pasternak, c. 1958 by Pantheon Books, a division of Random House. Used by Permission. All Rights Reserved.

Carl Sandburg, Prayers of Steel from *Cornhuskers,* c. 1918 bv Henry Holt and Company, c. 1946 by Carl Sandburg. "I Am the People," *Chicago Poems,* c. 1916 Henry Holt & Company, c. 1944 by Carl Sandburg. All rights reserved. Used by permission. Published by Holt Rinehart & Winston.

Tennessee Williams. "The Timeless World of a Play" and "The Rose Tatoo," c. 1950, 1951 by Tennessee Williams. "Battle of the Angels," c. 1940 by Tennessee Williams, "Orpheus Descending," c. 1955, 1958 by Tennessee Williams, "The Glass Menagerie," c. 1945,1948 Tennessee Williams. "Camino Real," c. 1948,1953 Tennessee Williams. "Person to Person," c. 1955 by Tennessee Williams. "The Glass Menagerie" is published by Random House. All others are published by New Directions Publishing Corporation, N.Y., N.Y. Used by Permission. All Rights Reserved.

All Biblical and Jewish liturgical texts are contemporary adaptations by the editors based on Hebrew texts. All musical texts, adaptations and translations, unless otherwise specified, are by the editors.

Art work: All photographs by David Coates, except the portrait of the editor by Kathleen Dowdey. All paintings and drawings are by the editor except for the portion of a mezzotint (p. 34) by Lynd Ward from the endpapers of a first edition copy of Oscar Wilde's "Ballad of Reading Gaol."

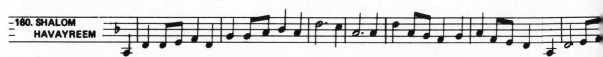

160. SHALOM HAVAYREEM

SONG TITLE INDEX

Abelchao	3
Ain't Gonna Let Nobody	
Turn Me Around	23
All Mixed Up	31
Amazing Love	59
America the Beautiful	79
Arise	46
Away Over Yonder	39
Battle Hymn of the Republic	52
Beautiful City	75
Because All Men Are Brothers	2
Birmingham Sunday	8
Bitter Was the Night 19	65
Blackbird	77
Blind Man	60
Break Bread Together	38
Bungalow Bill	66
Burn Baby Burn	47
A Child's Dream	77
Cities are Burnin'	9
Come and Go With Me	12
Come By Here	62
De Colores	74
Deep River	40
Deportees	64
Devil Wore a Crucifix	45
Eleanor Rigby	35
Enter, Rejoice and Come In	2
Everybody Loves Saturday Night	58
Everybody's Got a Right To Live	11
Filled With Life	74
Free At Last	81
Freedom	80
Freedom Now	59
Freedom Is a Constant Struggle	61
George Fox	21
Get on Board 48	77
Get Together	28
Glee Reigns in Galilee	53
Go Down Moses	3
Go Tell It on the Mountain	71
Go Where I send Thee	73
God Called Adam	55
God is Here	78
Golden Thread	33
Gonna Sing My Lord	25
Great Hallelu	76
Guantanamera	40
Hallelujah	79
Hard Travelin'	67
Hava Nagila	70
Help	60
Hide Your Heart Little Hippie	17
Hiney Matov	79
I Cannot Come	12
I Don't Want Your Millions Mister	42
I'm On My Way	50
I've Got That Joy	79
I Want To Be Ready	73
Idols of Silver and Gold	43
If I Had a Hammer	32
It Isn't Nice	51
It's Me	62
Jesus Christ	52
Johnny I Hardly Knew Ye	37
Jonah	5
Joshua	59
Joy to the World	72
Justicia En Marcha	25
Keep Your Eye on the Prize	23
La Bamba	27
La Peregrinacion	10
Laughin Fool	22
Lay Down My Sword and Shield	33
Lift Every Voice and Sing	54
Litany	64
Little Boxes	15
Livin' in All Men	24
Lonesome Traveller	42
Lonesome Valley	66
Lord of the Dance	12
Love Song	29
Love That is Hoarded	34
Man That Waters the Workers Beer	57
Mary Don't You Weep	24
Midnight Special	36
Mill Was Made of Marble	76
Michael Haul Your Boat Ashore	68
Mr. Blue	16
Morning Trumpet	4
Motherless Child	35
My Country 'Tis of Thy People	
Your Dying	6
A New Day	41
A New Song	43
Nowhere Man	19
O Come Emmanuel	37
O Freedom	26
O Healing River	63
Our Father	39
One Man's Hands	54
Pack Up Your Sorrows	17
A Piece of Ground	9
Pity the Downtrodden Landlord	58
Preacher and the Slave	7
Promises To Keep	54
Put It on the Ground	58
Ramblin' Boy	30
Respect	48
Rise Up Shepherd	72
Rockin' Jerusalem	14
Saints Go Marchin' In	80
Samson	47
Seek and You Shall Find	27
Seize Joy	27
Send Forth Your Spirit Lord	69
Ser Como El Aire Libre	66
Shalom Alechem	78
Shalom Havayreem	80
She's Leaving Home	48
Shout for Joy	70
Simple Gifts	44
Solidarity Forever	53
Solidaridad Por Siempre	53
Somebody's Knockin' at Your Door	45
Spirit is Movin'	13
Ta Ra Ra Boom Dee Ay	45
The Teacher's Lament	55
There But for Fortune	5
They Cast Their Nets in Galilee	67
Thirsty Boots	61
This Land is Your Land	75
This Little Light	71
Those Who Sow in Sorrow	68

Through the Bitter Land	11
Turn Turn Turn	49
Twelve Days of Christmas	70
Union Maid	22
Virgin Mary	70
Wade in the Water	21
Wake Up	51
War Department	78
Wayfarin' Stranger	41
Wearin' of the Green	56
We Can Work it Out	39
We Didn't Know	19
We Shall Overcome	25
We Shall Not Be Moved	27
We'll Never Turn Back	68
We're Gonna Move	74
We're Gonna Roll	13
Wedlock	32
Welcome Table	78
Well Respected Man	4
Were You There	64
What Did You Learn in School Today	44
What Does Your God Look Like	4
What's That I hear	1
When I First Came to This Land	55
When I Needed a Neighbor	8
Where Have All the Flowers Gone	37
Where You Gonna Run To	20
Which Side Are You On	57
Who Am I	10
The Whole World	26
Woke Up This Morning	25
Woman at the Well	18
The Word II	30
Yesterday	15
You've Got To Hide Your Love Away	16

Inquest	36
Keep Goin On	23
Killing	38
Kingdom of United Nations	78
Law and Order I	45
Law and Order II	46
Law and Order III	47
Listen!	2
The Lord Said to Moses	1
The Lord's Servant	3
Mama Parks	22
Man	71
A Martyr's Welcome	68
Movin' On	24
My God, My God	67
A New Generation	50
A New Life	43
A New People	41
No Man is an Island	35
Not To Cry	17
Not To Feel	16
Novocain	7
Odds	26
The One Essential	23
Out of the Depths	65
The Partnership	54
Prayer	38
Prayer	58
Prayer for Brotherhood	33
Prayer of Steel	53
Precious Death	68
The Proud Trampled Underfoot by the Needy	75
The Rebel	10
Release	18
Remember	62
Revenge	44
Revolutionary World	49
Richard Cory	36
Safety of Slavery	16
Sharing of Bread	30
Solitary Confinement	35
Strength	61
Suffering Servant	5
Tear Down the Idols	45
Three Hundred Years	46
To Hide	19
To Lie	18
To Run	15
To Tell the Truth	20
To Tremble	15
Tyranny	57
Uhuru	1
Velvet Violence	48
We're Lonely	32
Within You, Without You	2
The Word I	29
The Word III	31

TITLE INDEX OF CHANTS AND READINGS

Abraham and Sarah	69
Atonement	38
Baptism	69
Be Yourself	21
Bread	4
Cleanse Me	38
The Confidence Cure	27
Creation	70
Dreamers	11
Dying	18
Father DeLeo	39
The Fool	75
Forever	56
The Gathered Bread	77
Glory	32
Golden Apples	42
The Hardest Thing	8
The Helping Hand	26
How It Feels	6
I Love You	28
Innocent Servant	8

AUTHOR AND COMPOSER INDEX

Eric Anderson,
Thirsty Boots   61
M.J. Archer & A.D. Rosetti,
A New People   41
James Baldwin   84
Ewald Bash, Jonah   5
Katherine Lee Bates & Samuel A. Ward,
America the Beautiful   79
Bay Singers   22
Lerone Bennett, Jr.   90
Daniel Berrigan   8, 33
Bible   See folk music and literature index
John Borger   64
Oscar Brand,
When I First Came to This Land   55
Justice Louis D. Brandeis   92
Etienne Briere,
Those Who Sow In Sorrow   68
Build Black, Inc.   23, 46
Richard J. Carr   66
Sydney Carter,
When I Needed a Neighbor   8
Lord of the Dance   12
George Fox   21
Devil Wore a Crucifix   45
Bitter Was the Night   19   66
Al Capone   45
Stokely Carmichael   53
Len Chandler,
Hide Your Heart Little Hippie   17
Ralph Chaplin, Solidarity Forever   53
Teillard de Chardin   73
Arnold Clayton,
Pity the Downtrodden Landlord   58
Eldridge Cleaver   28
Jean Cocteau   52
Jimmy Collier, Burn Baby Burn   47
Alex Comfort, One Man's Hands   54
Jim Connell, Arise!   46
Coroner's Inquest   36, 62, 65
Cardinal Cushing   68
Halim El Dabh   85
R. Davies, A Well Respected Man   4
Ossie Davis, On Malcolm X   20, 40
Diana Dew   50
John Donne   35
Justice W. O. Douglas   47
Frederick Douglass   51, 55, 92, 93
L. G. Dowdey   15, 18, 64, 82
Alexander Dubchek   67
W. E. B. DuBois   18, 21, 40, 42, 92
Duke Ellington   108
Richard Farina,
Birmingham Sunday   8
Pack Up Your Sorrows   17
Folk Music   See Separate Index
Felix Frankfurter   79
Erich Fromm   83
Senator J.W. Fulbright   42
Freedom songs   See folk music & lit. index
Esther Galli,
Fuertes Somos Ya   27
Las Machinas Eran de Oro   76
M. K. Gandhi   4

Jim Garland,
I Don't Want Your Millions Mister   42
Marcus Garvey   22
Ray Glaser, Put It on the Ground   58
Joe Glazer,
Teacher's Lament   55
Mill Was Made of Marble   76
A Child's Dream   77
Tom Glazer,
Because All Men Are Brothers   2
Bertha Gober,
We'll Never Turn Back   68
Ozzie Gontang, Dying   18
Father Antonio Gonzales,
Justicia En Marcha   25
Dick Gregory   78
Allene Guss Grognet   76, 79
Che Guevara   67
Woodie Guthrie,
Union Maid   22
Jesus Christ   52
Deportees   64
Hard Travelin   67
This Land is Your Land   75
J. F. Handel, Hallelujah Chorus   79
George Harrison,
Within You, Without You   2
John Hart   83
William Hastie   54
Alfred Hayes, Joe Hill   61
Lee Hayes, If I Had a Hammer   32
Fred Hellerman & Fran Minkof,
O Healing River   63
Joe Hill,   86
Preacher and the Slave   7
Ta Ra Ra Boom Dee Ay   45
Justice Oliver Wendall Homes, Jr.
Inside back cover
Cisco Houston   90
Julia Ward Howe & William Staffa,
Battle Hymn of the Republic   52
George Pullen Jackson   94
Pope John XXIII   46, 73
Charles S. Johnson   91
James Weldon & J. Rosamund Johnson,
Lift Every Voice and Sing   54
James Joyce   31
Jacqueline Kennedy   61
John F. Kennedy   55, 59
Robert F. Kennedy   23, 49, 72, 74
Corita Kent   71, 74, 82
Denmark Vesey   91
Martin Luther King   66, 81
Frederick Douglass Kirkpatrick,
The Cities Are Burnin'   9
Everybody's Got a Right to Live   11
Laughin' Fool   22
Halper Leivick, Forever   56
John Lennon & Paul McCartney,
Yesterday   15
You've Got to Hide Your Love Away   16
Nowhere Man   19
The Word   30
Eleanor Rigby   35
We Can Work It Out   39
She's Leaving Home   48
Blackbird   77
Bungalow Bill   65

Help	60
Augustin Lira, La Peregrinacion	10
Konrad Lorenz	60
James Russell Lowell	61
Malcolm X	7, 26, 30
Pauline Marden,	
Pack Up Your Sorrows	17
Jose Marti, Guantanamera	40
Patrick Mason,	
What Does Your God Look Like	4
Rufus (Catfish) Mayfield	62, 65
Joe McDonald, Who Am I	10
Ann Marie McLoone, Promises to Keep	54
James Minchin,	
O Come Emmanuel	37
Maria Montessori	43, 48
Mother Scott, God Called Adam	55
Free At Last	81
Phil Ochs,	
What's That I Hear	1
There But for Fortune	5
Olatunji, Uhuru	1
Thomas Paine	57
Boris Pasternak	63
Tom Paxton, Mr. Blue	16
We Didn't Know	19
Ramblin' Boy	30
What Did You Learn in School Today	44
Padriac Pearce, The Rebel	10
The Fool	75
W. A. Percy,	
They Cast Their Nets in Galilee	67
Chet Powers, Get Together	28
Paul Quinlan, Great Hallelu	76
Otis Redding, Respect	48
Florence Reece,	
Which Side Are You On?	57
Malvina Reynolds,	
Little Boxes	15
It Isn't Nice	51
Les Rice, A New Day	41
Clarence Rivers, Out of the Depths	65
Edward Arlington Robinson,	
Richard Cory	36

Louise Ruspini	
Enter, Rejoice and Come In	2
Paddy Ryan,	
Man That Waters the Workers' Beer	57
Buffy St. Marie,	
My Country Tis of Thy People You're Dying	6
Carl Sandburg	27, 53
George Santayana	44
Pete Seeger, All Mixed Up	31
If I Had a Hammer	32
Golden Thread	33
Where Have All the Flowers Gone	37
Turn, Turn, Turn	49
One Man's Hands	54
John Snyder, Spirit is Moving	13
Wayfaring Stranger	41
Spirituals　　　See folk music index	
Jeremy Taylor, Piece of Ground	9
Harry S. Truman	58
Harriet Tubman	26
Louis Untermeyer	58
Isaac Watts, Joy to the World	72
Oscar Wilde	38
Tennessee Williams,	
From:	
Battle of the Angels	2
Orpheus Descending	6, 41, 70, 72
Camino Real	11, 24, 29, 32, 38
Timeless World of a Play	16, 35
Rose Tatoo	17, 32, 39, 59
Glass Menagerie	27
Miriam Therese Winter, I Cannot Come	12
Joe Wise, Gonna Sing My Lord	25
Bill Wolf,	
Put It on the Ground	58
B. Woolf,	
Pity the Downtrodden Landlord	58
Yevgeny Yevtushenko	19, 69

FOLK SONGS AND LITERATURE

Arranged, Adapted and Translated
by the editors.

Abelachao	3
Ain't Gonna Let Nobody Turn Me Around	23
Amazing Love	59
Away Over Yonder	39
Beautiful City	75
Bible	
Canticles 1,2,4,7,8	29
Deut. 7	26, 39, 45
Deut. 8	62
Ecclesisties 3	49
Exodus 3,4,5	1
Exodus 14	16, 23
Exodus 19	54
Genesis 4	37
Genesis 12	41
Genesis 17,18,21	69
Habakkuk	4
Isaiah	4
Isaiah 3,10,26	75
Isaiah 11	78
Isaiah 35	61
Isaiah 42,49	3
Isaiah 51	51
Isaiah 52	51
Isaiah 53	5, 8
Isaiah 58	38
Isaiah 58,65	41
Isaiah 60	51
Isaiah 61	11, 51
Jeremiah	4
Luke 1	74
Psalms 8, 139	71
Psalm 22	67
Psalms 32, 139	18
Psalms 38,51	38
Psalm 55	15
Psalm 84	11
Psalm 85	11
Psalm 94	44
Psalms 95-99	43
Psalms 104, 72, 85	69
Psalm 105	11
Psalm 113	76
Psalm 115	43
Psalm 116	68
Psalm 130	65
Romans	23, 51
St. John (Revelation)	4
Blind Man Stood in the Road and Cried	60
Break Bread Together	38
Come and Go With Me	12
Come By Here	62
De Colores	74
Deep River	40
Didache	77
Everybody Loves Saturday Night	58
Freedom	80
Freedom Now	59
Freedom Is a Constant Struggle	61
Get on Board	48 77
Glee Reigns in Galilee	53
Go Down Moses	3
Go Tell It On the Mountain	71
Go Where I Send Thee	73
God is Here	78
Hava Nagila	70
Hiney Matov	79
I Want to Be Ready	73
Idols of Silver and Gold	43
I'm On My Way	50
I've Got That Joy	79
It's Me	62
Johnny I Hardly Knew Ye	37
Joshua	59
Keep Your Eye on the Prize	23
La Bamba	27
Lay Down My Sword and Shield	33
Living in All Men	24
Lonesome Traveller	42
Lonesome Valley	66
Love That is Hoarded	34
Mary Don't You Weep	24
Michael	68
Midnight Special	36
Morning Trumpet	4
Motherless Child	35
O Come Emmanuel	37
O Freedom	26
Our Father	39
Passover Prayer	30
Passover Prayer	80
Prayer for Brotherhood	33
Prayer	43
Rise Up Shepherd	72
Rockin' Jerusalem	14
Shalom Alechem	78
Shalom Havayreem	80
Saints Go Marchin' In	80
Samson	47
Seek and You Shall Find	27
Seize Joy	27
Ser Como El Aire Libre	66
Shout For Joy	70
Simple Gifts	44
Somebody's Knockin at Your Door	45
Spirit is Movin'	13
This Little Light	71
Through the Bitter Land	11
Twelve Days of Christmas	70
Uhuru	1
Virgin Mary	70
Wade in the Water	21
Wake Up!	51
War Department	78
Wayfaring Stranger	41
We Shall Not Be Moved	27
We Shall Overcome	25
We're Gonna Move	74
We're Gonna Roll	13
Wearin' of the Green	56
Wedlock	32
Welcome Table	78
Were You There	64
Where You Gonna Run To?	20
Whole World	26
Woke Up This Morning	25
Woman at the Well	18

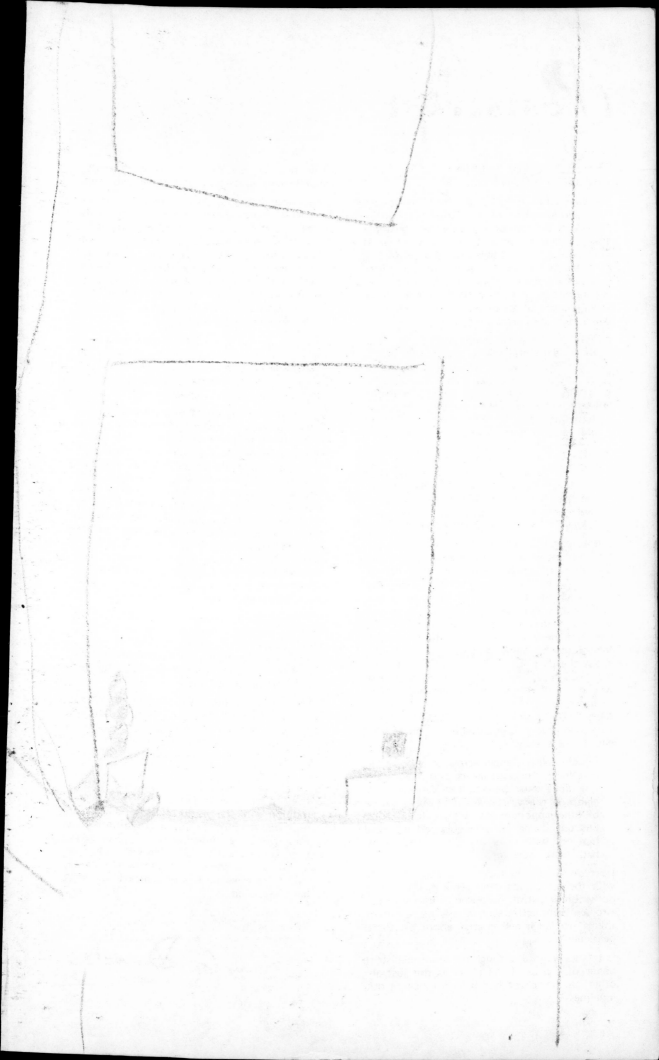